'Over the years I've learned that you have this endearing ability to spot a chance to make a profit further than a leopard can spot a limp,' Jake said.

'Why must you always believe the worst of me?' Shiona demanded.

'Perhaps because it's so easy to believe the worst of you.' Jake smiled a slow smile as his eyes swept over her, and one hand reached up suddenly to cup her chin.

'Look at that mouth.' His thumb brushed her lips, sending prickles of sensitivity quivering through her. 'That is the mouth of a temptress, a seductress. A mouth that was made for lies—and kissing.'

Books you will enjoy
by STEPHANIE HOWARD

ROMANTIC JOURNEY

Vittorio de Esquerez denigrated Kate's journalism and the serious magazine for which she worked; just because he was wealthy and successful, he thought he could walk over anyone who got in his way. But she'd show him—she desperately needed to get her story, and she intended to get it, no matter what!

KISS AND SAY GOODBYE

Eve Adams felt that at last everything was beginning to go right for her—she had the perfect country cottage, and even a charming, handsome neighbour. But then the arrogant Rodrigo Garcia Marquez came into her life— and everything became much more complicated!

A MATTER OF HONOUR

It was vital that Beth find her stepbrother, Giles—that was why she had come to Italy. The last thing she needed was to be haunted by Lorenzo dei Cesari. After all, she had been warned about him. So why should it hurt so much that he clearly despised her?

DANGEROUS INFATUATION

There were simply no words to describe adequately Angela's feelings about Sheikh Rashid al-Hazar. He thought he could do what he wanted, when he wanted and how he wanted. And he wanted her out of the country. But she had no intention of giving up her job on his paper—even if it meant putting up with his male arrogance!

BATTLE FOR LOVE

BY
STEPHANIE HOWARD

MILLS & BOON LIMITED
ETON HOUSE   18–24 PARADISE ROAD
RICHMOND   SURREY   TW9 1SR

First published in Great Britain 1991 by Mills & Boon Limited

© Stephanie Howard 1991

*Australian copyright 1991
Philippine copyright 1992
This edition 1992*

ISBN 0 263 77306 X

*Set in 10 on 12 pt Linotron Palatino
91-9202-48628
Typeset in Great Britain by Centracet, Cambridge
Made and printed in Great Britain*

CHAPTER ONE

SHIONA was watching from an upstairs window when the car appeared at the foot of the driveway.

Instantly, she felt herself tense and the butterflies in her stomach grow stronger, as the immaculately shiny black Mercedes headed swiftly for the forecourt below her and drew to a halt with a splutter of gravel.

She glanced at her watch. He was a few minutes early. Clearly, he was anxious to see her, and that, she sensed, could only mean trouble.

'Don't worry, I'll get it.' As she turned to leave the room, she caught sight of Inge hovering out on the landing.

'Thanks, Miss Fergusson. Is it OK if I leave now?' The plump au pair blushed a little coyly. 'I have an appointment in the village.'

'Of course it's OK.' Shiona smiled kindly. 'Just do me one favour before you go. Tell Nettie that Mr MacKay has arrived, and ask her to be good enough to bring us some tea.'

'Of course, Miss Fergusson.' The blonde girl nodded and headed swiftly for the stairs.

'Oh, and Inge. . .' Shiona stepped out on to the landing. 'Be sure to pick up Kirsty from school at four.'

'I won't forget.' As Inge plunged down the stairs

and headed for the kitchen at the back of the house, Shiona watched her go with an almost envious smile. If only I was as carefree right now, she was thinking.

Then, bracing herself, she strode to the top of the staircase and stood gazing down the wide, sweeping curve of it to the imposing hallway and the big front door. I shall wait until he rings before opening, she decided. No need for him to know that I was watching at the window.

She started down the stairs, her steps deliberately unhurried, breathing deeply to calm her twanging nerves, and paused for an instant to scrutinise her reflection in the massive gilt-framed mirror that hung above the banisters.

A pale oval face with wide hazel eyes and a halo of shoulder-length auburn hair, as bright as burnished copper, stared back serious and unblinking. She gave herself a shake. No need to look so anxious. Whatever he's come for, he's not going to eat you!

She pinched her cheeks quickly to add a little colour, and straightened the skirt of her plum-coloured sweater-dress before squaring her slim shoulders and resuming her descent.

Not only was he not going to eat her, she thought crisply, he would not even manage to unnerve her. These days she was more than a match for his bullying!

A few steps from the foot of the crimson-carpeted staircase Shiona paused, her eyes fixed on the front door. Any second now he would ring the doorbell in his usual autocratic, impatient manner. But she would wait a full minute at least before answering. She wasn't his little slave girl any longer.

But in that very same instant, momentarily demolishing her composure, the door burst open with the force of an explosion and a tall dark-haired figure in a charcoal-grey suit came striding purposefully into the hall.

He paused at the foot of the stairs to look up at her. 'How very thoughtful of you to hurry down to greet me. I hadn't expected so eager a welcome.'

Of course. He had a key. Stupidly, she had forgotten that. Her expression far from eager, Shiona looked back at him. 'Hello, Jake,' she offered. 'You made it, I see.'

'Of course I made it. Why wouldn't I have made it?' He had come to lean against the foot of the banisters, looking up at her with a spark of challenge in his eyes. 'Were you perhaps hoping that I might fail to keep our appointment?'

Shiona suppressed a mirthless smile. He had read her mind with perfect accuracy. When his solicitor had phoned to make the appointment, refusing to say why his client wished to see her, she had secretly prayed that fate might intervene and mercifully save her from this meeting.

She had seen him only once during the past three years—two bleak weeks ago at the funeral, when her grief had been so great that she had barely registered his presence. And she had sincerely hoped that that would be their last meeting ever.

Now she let her eyes travel over his arrogant face— the aquiline nose, the wide caustic mouth, the

straight black eyebrows, the firm aggressive chin—
and hated the way her heart quivered inside her.
Once, she would have laid down her life for this
man, and the memory of that devotion could still
make her soul weep.

But as she shifted her gaze back to his eyes—eyes
as brightly blue as the bluest summer sky and such a
startling contrast with his almost-black hair—that
momentary tremor inside her was extinguished. She
remembered how cruelly those eyes could look at
her, turning her blood to vinegar in her veins. And
the memory strengthened the hatred within her.

In a cool voice she answered, 'I thought you might
be late. You have come quite a distance, after all.
New York isn't exactly just a few miles down the
road.'

'I got back from New York late last night.' The blue
eyes watched her from beneath long black lashes. 'It
took me just over an hour to drive here from
Edinburgh.'

'I'm surprised you found your way. You're such
an infrequent visitor. These days you seem to spend
most of your time in the States.'

He smiled at that. 'I spend a fair amount of time
there.' Then the smile altered slightly. He raised one
dark eyebrow. 'How very flattering, my dear Shiona,
that you should keep such a careful check on my
movements.'

Shiona grimaced in response. 'Please don't feel
flattered.' How she hated the way he called her 'my
dear Shiona'. The false endearment grated on her

nerves. 'If I kept a careful check on your move-ments—which I don't—I can assure you it would not be for sentimental reasons.'

Jake held her eyes. 'Don't worry,' he parried. 'It would never for one moment cross my mind to accuse you of being a sentimentalist.' He stepped back from the banisters. 'But enough of these pleas-antries. I suggest we make ourselves comfortable and get down to business.'

As he spoke, he had already turned abruptly on his heel and was leading her in swift strides across the wide hallway. Then he was sweeping through the doorway of the main reception-room, with Shiona having to hurry in order to keep pace with him.

She glared at his back, hating him warmly—the self-assured set of the broad, powerful shoulders, the unfaltering step of those lean athlete's legs. Every-thing he did seemed like a statement of his authority. Even the simple act of crossing a room.

But what was this business he had referred to? What was this meeting supposed to be about?

Before she could ask, he paused in mid-stride, so that she almost went crashing right into him. 'Shall we sit by the window?' he enquired, glancing down at her. Then, without bothering to wait for her answer, he had swung round again and was heading imperiously for the group of gold-brocade-covered armchairs that stood in the curve of the huge bay window, overlooking the sun-burnished waters of Loch Lomond.

'How beautiful it is at this time of the year.' He

paused for a moment to glance out of the window. Then he turned back to Shiona. 'But, I'm forgetting. . .' His eyes lit up with a mocking little smile. 'The rustic delights of a Scottish spring aren't really to your taste. You're a big-city girl. What you love are all those glitzy London shops where you can indulge your weakness for expensive baubles.'

The malice in his tone scraped at Shiona's nerve-ends. So, he was at it already, she thought, straightening her shoulders. The same old accusations, the same scathing comments. But he was mistaken if he thought that he could upset her. Nothing Jake might say could upset her any more.

Averting her gaze, Shiona sat down in one of the armchairs, smoothing the skirt of her dress over her knees. 'You're right, I enjoy my life in London. As a city it has a great deal to offer—especially to someone like myself who works in the rag trade. But I also love it here.' She swivelled her eyes round and paused for a moment as they meshed with Jake's. 'Why else would I have set up my workshop near Killearn?'

'Why else, indeed?' His tone was sharp with irony. 'I suggest *you* know the answer to that one.'

'And what are you implying?'

'Implying? Nothing. But let's just say it has crossed my mind to wonder why you were so keen to keep a foothold in this part of the world.'

'It used to be my home.'

'Only very briefly. You only lived here for a couple of years.'

'I lived here for three years, if you want to be

precise.' Shiona's tone was tight with resentment.
She narrowed her eyes and added in clipped tones,
'I know you always thought of this as *your* home and
that you never wanted me to be a part of it. But, like
it or not, it became my home too, the moment your
father married my mother.'

At the mention of her mother, her tone suddenly
faltered and a pain like a lance went driving through
her. It had still barely sunk in that just over two
weeks ago her mother and her stepfather had been
killed in an accident.

Her eyes dropped to her lap. She stared at her
hands. 'Another reason for setting up my workshop
near here was so that I wouldn't lose touch with my
mother.'

'And my father. Let's not forget my father—the
goose who laid the golden eggs.'

He was still standing over her, his back to the
window, so that his features were shrouded in
shadow. 'Well, your devotion paid off.' His tone was
cynical. 'You now have a half-share in my father's
house.'

What a foul suggestion! 'How dare you say that?'
Quivering with anger, Shiona turned to glare at him.
'I happened to be extremely fond of your father!'

'Of course you were. And even fonder of his
money. You were extremely fond of all the MacKay
men—and they all let you wrap them round your
little finger. With one significant exception, of
course.' He paused and laughed roughly beneath his
breath. 'But then, I, my dear Shiona, saw through
you from the start.'

Jake had been hurling these same insults at her now for years, and by now she ought to be totally immune to them. But, ridiculously, they still hurt as much as ever. The poison in his words burned like gall through Shiona's veins. The only difference now was that she did not show it. She had failed to acquire immunity, but she had learned to fake it.

'You're wrong about one thing.' Shiona eyed him harshly. 'I was fond of your father and I was fond of your brother, but I can't say I was ever the least bit fond of you.'

'You cared about none of us!' He dashed her claim aside. 'All you ever cared about was what you could get out of us! Well, you've had all you're getting, my sweet little stepsister, and that's the reason I'm here today—to assure you that I intend to finally put an end to your grubby manoeuvres to extract money from my family!'

As her cheeks paled visibly, he went on without mercy, 'You may have succeeded in getting your greedy little hooks into my father and my brother, but you're never going to get them into my sister. So you can forget right now any ambitions you might have as far as Kirsty is concerned!'

'What sort of ambitions? What are you suggesting?' Suddenly Shiona was trembling with outrage, but her tone was as cool as tempered steel as she told him, 'The only ambition I have regarding Kirsty is to be appointed as her legal guardian!'

'That's what I mean.'

As his eyes drove into her, she had a sudden sharp insight in to what he was here for. She narrowed her eyes at him and warned him icily, 'If you've come here with some idea of trying to block my petition to become Kirsty's guardian, I warn you right now you're wasting your time!'

As she said it her heart tugged with emotion at the thought of her five-year-old little sister, the daughter of Jake's father and her own mother, so recently and so tragically orphaned.

She looked Jake in the eye and demanded flatly, '*Is* that the reason why you're here?'

But, alas, she was destined to have to wait for an answer, as Nettie, the housekeeper, chose that very moment to come into the room carrying a tea-tray.

Oblivious of the anger that crackled in the air, she cast a welcoming smile in Jake's direction. 'It's nice to see you again, Mr MacKay.'

'It's nice to be here,' he replied with a composed smile, seating himself at last in one of the armchairs, as the woman arranged the tea things on a small table in front of them. 'I was just saying to Miss Fergusson how very beautiful it is.'

Shiona darted him a quick look, her heart still pounding. Who would ever guess from the benign expression on his face that just a moment ago he had been exploding with anger? He was like a chameleon, she thought with wry admiration, able to adapt at will to any situation. Which was why, of course, no one else had ever guessed at just how much he had always loathed her. The expression of that loathing had been reserved exclusively for her.

And yet for years I adored him, she thought with horrified wonder. For years I allowed him to treat me like dirt. But he's wrong if he thinks he can push me around now. Those bad old days are gone for good.

She raised her eyes to Nettie, her composure equal to Jake's now. 'Don't worry, Nettie, I'll do the honours.' She reached for the teapot and poured without a tremor. 'Thanks,' she smiled, as the woman turned to leave.

When they were left alone, a silence descended, broken only by the click of silver against porcelain as Jake helped himself to sugar and stirred. Shiona picked up her own cup and sat back in her seat, eyeing Jake over the rim as she raised the cup and drank. Then she laid the cup down again and turned pointedly to look at him.

'We were talking about Kirsty,' she prompted in a cool tone. Yet her heart fluttered anxiously inside her as she said it. What exactly had he meant by that stupid, spiteful threat?

'That's right, we were.' His eyes slid round to look at her, but he did not pursue his earlier tirade. Instead, he cast his gaze round the room where they were sitting. 'Naturally,' he informed her, 'I intend to buy you out.'

That threw her totally. 'Buy me out of what?'

'The house, my dear Shiona. Your share of the house. As you are aware, my father left half of it to each of us.' He smiled without humour. 'A most unfortunate arrangement. Surely he can't have imagined that we would wish to live together?'

What an abominable prospect! Shiona pulled a face. Then she informed him crisply, 'But I don't intend to sell.'

Jake sighed a little impatiently. 'I'll pay you a good price. You don't have to haggle. I don't intend to cheat you.'

'I'm not interested in your price. I don't intend selling. In fact. . .' She paused. 'You've given me an idea. I would much prefer to buy your share from you.'

'What the devil for?' His impatience was growing. 'Stop playing silly games and just accept my offer. The house means nothing to you. I'm sure you'd much prefer the money.'

He really did believe that money was all she cared about! Shiona felt her hackles rise in anger. 'I don't want your damned money and I don't intend selling! You're wasting your time by trying to persuade me!'

'And why won't you sell?' Jake's tone had grown flinty. 'What good is half a house in the middle of Scotland to someone who spends all her time down in London?'

'I don't spend all my time down in London! That just shows how little you know about my affairs! I make frequent visits to the Killearn workshop and I need a base for when I'm in Scotland. In the past I've always stayed here at Lomond View, and that's precisely what I intend to carry on doing!'

Jake sat back in his chair. 'OK, so you need a base, but surely you don't need one quite as big as this?' As he spoke, with forced patience, he stabbed his fingers through his hair and narrowed his eyes at her in irritation. 'With the money I'm prepared to pay you for your half of the house you could buy a more than adequate little base for yourself—and still have change left to indulge in a few luxuries.'

He smiled condescendingly. 'Just think,' he told her, 'you could treat yourself to a trip down Bond Street and splurge on a few trinkets and some new clothes for your wardrobe.'

'How kind of you to be so preoccupied with my needs.' Shiona's tone was heavy with sarcasm. 'But I've already told you you're wasting your time. I haven't the remotest intention of selling.'

'And why would that be?' The blue eyes narrowed thoughtfully. 'Perhaps, after all, you really do secretly relish the thought of sharing a house with me.' He let his eyes travel over her, openly appraising, as his gaze took in the firm, high breasts, softly moulded by the cashmere of her sweater-dress, then drifted down to the dip of her waist and the womanly curves of her hips and thighs.

'Is that what's behind this strategy of yours? Are you hoping to get to know your stepbrother better?'

In spite of herself, Shiona was aware of a warming of her skin from her scalp to her toes, and her reaction both humiliated and angered her. It reminded her of the old days when just a passing glance of his could reduce her to a state of burning confusion.

She pulled herself together, swallowing hard, and forced herself to look him straight in the face. 'I already know you as well as I could ever want to. And besides, it would take a stronger stomach than mine to contemplate furthering our acquaintance.'

As he simply smiled at her reaction, she hurried

on to ask a question of her own. 'But surely you're not intending to move in here permanently? You already have a house in Edinburgh.'

'I already have several houses, my dear Shiona. And, no—I'm sorry if this disappoints you—I'm not planning to move in here on a permanent basis. But it would make rather a lovely weekend home.'

'A little large for one, surely,' she countered, taking pleasure in turning his own words against him. 'Wouldn't it be more sensible to sell your share to me and buy yourself a smaller place?' She fixed her hazel eyes on his and elaborated, smiling, 'You could treat yourself to a few trinkets with the change.'

He smiled back at her briefly, but his eyes remained hostile. 'It is you, not I, who have a penchant for trinkets. Particularly when you don't have to earn the money to pay for them.' Then, before she had a chance to rebut that accusation, he added, 'And besides, I really wasn't planning to spend my weekends here alone.'

I'll bet you weren't! Shiona smiled thinly, but refrained from voicing her suspicions out loud. What did it matter to her, after all, that he no doubt planned to entertain his ladyfriends here?

Instead, she assured him. 'Neither was I. The reason I intend to keep my stake in this house is so that Kirsty and I can use it when we come up to Scotland.' She paused. 'Which brings us back to what we were speaking about. . . Kirsty and my application for custody.'

She looked straight into his face. 'I asked you a

question and I'm still waiting for your answer. Do you intend to stand in my way?'

He smiled a veiled smile and sat back in his seat. 'Yes, as a matter of fact, I do.'

'You can't be serious!'

'I'm afraid I'm most serious.'

'But why?' Shiona frowned at him with irritation. 'Why on earth would you want to do that? Who do you expect to look after her if not me?'

His gaze never flickered. 'Me,' he answered.

But that was preposterous! 'You? You're joking! You're never in the country! How can you possibly look after her?'

Jake did not answer her question directly. He flicked imaginary dust from the sleeve of his jacket and informed her, 'As you must surely be aware, Kirsty has already been placed in my custody.'

'Temporarily,' Shiona hastened to remind him. 'Only an interim custody order has been granted. The court has still to make its final decision.'

'Which, in due course, it will make in favour of me.'

Shiona could scarcely believe what she was hearing. She swallowed. 'I find it hard to believe you're serious. I was surprised when I found out about the interim order, but I assumed that was only a convenience measure, because you're resident in Scotland and I'm not. It never occurred to me that you intended to apply for permanent custody.'

She cleared her throat. 'I don't know why you're doing it, but it strikes me as being quite inappropriate.'

Jake looked back at her levelly. 'I have many reasons for doing it, the principal among them quite simply being to ensure that you never get your hands on my sister. That would really be "inappropriate".'

So he was acting out of spite. Anger welled up in her. 'You're despicable! Would you really play around with a five-year-old's future just because you have a grudge against me?'

He was unrepentant. 'You, my dear Shiona, are the one who has plans to play around with her future. All I'm doing is protecting her—from you.'

She couldn't let that pass. Not a second time. Shiona thrust up her chin and looked straight at him. 'Kindly explain what you mean by that.'

Jake shook his head impatiently. 'Don't play the innocent. We both know exactly what I mean.'

'I'm afraid I don't.' That was not quite truthful. She had learned how to read Jake like a book. But she refused to let him off with insinuations. If he had something to say, let him come out and say it!

Relentlessly she pressed him. 'Kindly explain.'

With a sigh of impatience Jake leaned back in his seat and ran his fingers through his thick dark hair. 'OK, I'll spell it out to you, if that's what you want. My father left Kirsty a considerable amount of money to be held in trust until she reaches eighteen. . .' He paused. 'Do I really need to go any further?'

'I'm afraid you do.' She would not let him off the hook. 'I haven't the least idea what you're getting at.'

Jake shrugged. 'OK. If you insist.' He laid his arms along the arms of the chair, his long, tanned fingers cupping the curved ends. 'Let me put it as delicately as I can. I don't wish to offend you any more than I need to. . .'

Shiona smiled cynically. You had to hand it to him. He could play the good guy so convincingly. Little wonder that, once, she'd been totally taken in. Then she tensed as, after a brief pause, he continued.

'A girl of eighteen is highly impressionable, easily influenced by those who are close to her—particularly in matters relating to money. Few young people have much business sense. . .'

Shiona nodded. 'I would agree with that.' She lifted her eyebrows. 'So, what are you saying?'

'What I'm saying is this. . .' The blue eyes pierced through her with that cold, callous look that once was capable of breaking her heart. 'If you were, as you were hoping to be, her legal custodian, you would be in a very powerful position—and I have reason to fear that you might abuse that power.'

She had known he would say that, but still her heart was thundering. 'Abuse it in what manner?' she heard herself asking.

'Come, come, my dear Shiona. You know perfectly well what I'm talking about. We both know that if you were ever to find yourself in such an influential position, my sister's inheritance would not long remain her own.'

It took all of Shiona's strength to keep her body from trembling. She would not let him see how much he had offended her. That would only give him pleasure.

She counted to ten inwardly. 'You're so damned predictable. Don't you ever get tired of insulting me?'

'You demanded the truth and now you've got it. It's not my fault if the truth happens to be unpleasant.' He smiled a false smile. 'Believe me, my dear Shiona, if I could, I'd much prefer to say something pleasant.'

'*You* say something pleasant to *me*? I'm sure you'd sooner cut out your tongue!'

As he smiled with cool amusement—without denying it, she noted—Shiona added, 'However, what you said was not the truth. It was just a vicious slander, based on nothing more substantial than your obsessive dislike of me!'

'Oh, no, my dear Shiona, it's based on much more than that.' Jake leaned forward in his seat to fix her with a look. 'Over the years I've learned that you have this endearing ability to spot a chance to make a profit further than a leopard can spot a limp. You ruined my brother. You left him penniless. You won't get a chance to do that to Kirsty!'

'I did not ruin your brother!' That was a mean and vicious slander. 'All I did was try to help him!'

'Oh, sure, you helped him! You helped him to spend his money! As we both know, that's something you're exceedingly good at.' His blue eyes flayed her, as he demanded harshly, 'Do you deny that he died with barely a penny to his name?'

She could not deny that. Shiona shook her head stiffly.

'And do you deny that for the two years prior to

his death you'd been living with him in his flat in London?'

'We shared the same house, but we weren't living together. Not in the way you're trying to suggest.'

'Liar!' Impatiently, Jake sprang to his feet. 'I've heard all these pathetic lies of yours before—but the facts of the matter speak for themselves. When you moved in with Ryan he was a wealthy man. By the time he died he was financially ruined. Parties, holidays, trips abroad. . . God knows the ways you found to help him fritter away his fortune.'

He bent suddenly to imprison her, his hands gripping the arms of her chair, his face thrust forwards furiously, inches from hers. 'Where are all the presents he no doubt bought you? The jewels, the diamonds, the baubles you're so fond of? Do you have them locked away in a bank vault? Do you take them out from time to time and gloat?'

What he was saying was horrible, and miles from the truth. And it struck Shiona, not for the first time, as she looked into those blue, accusing eyes, how easy it would be for her to clear her name.

He was so sure he was right, so sure he knew everything, so absolutely certain she deserved his dislike. But if she'd wanted to she could easily have told him something that would have stopped him dead in his tracks. That she chose to remain silent was out of loyalty—just one of the many little attributes that, according to him, she did not possess.

She faced his dislike now without flinching, and answered in as calm a voice as she could manage, 'I can assure you Ryan never bought me anything—

certainly not all these diamonds you keep inventing.'
Then, as he shook his head at her disbelievingly, she
demanded, 'Why must you always believe the worst
of me?'

'Perhaps because it's so easy to believe the worst
of you.' He smiled a slow smile as his eyes swept
over her, and one hand reached up suddenly to cup
her chin.

'Look at that mouth.' His thumb brushed her lips,
sending prickles of sensitivity quivering through her.
'That is the mouth of a temptress, a seductress. A
mouth that was made for lies—and kissing.'

As he paused, Shiona felt a sudden rush of anxiety.
Surely he wouldn't. . .? Her heart tightened within
her.

But he made no move to close the gap between
them, as his deep blue gaze continued to caress her.

'And this hair. . .' He let his fingers tangle in its
brightness, sending jolts of electricity skittering
across her scalp. 'This is the hair of a wild free spirit,
full of secret, sensuous promise. A man might sell
his soul just to bury his face in it.'

He lifted up a handful of burnished tawny curls
and let them slide silkily through his fingers. 'The
hair, too, you see, is the hair of a temptress.'

His eyes seemed to darken as his gaze slid lower.
'This body is the body of a temptress also.' And, as
his hand moved downwards, Shiona shrank back in
her chair, every muscle in her body tensing.

But he did not touch her, though it felt as though
he had, as his hand curved round the outline of her
breast. And to her shame and horror Shiona felt her

nipples tighten and press hard against the softness of her dress.

This unfortunate development did not go unnoticed. A wolfish smile lit up his eyes.

'I see you also have the soul of a temptress. It is clearly something beyond your control.' He touched her mouth again with the flat of his thumb, making her heart thud strangely inside her. 'You make it very difficult for any man to resist you. No wonder my poor brother fell under your spell.'

'It wasn't like that.' At last she found her voice and struggled to sit upright in her chair. Just for a moment there he had seemed to hypnotise her. Even now she felt oddly drugged by her nearness to him.

Jake smiled disbelievingly. 'More lies, my sweet temptress? But your lies, alas, will get you nowhere with me.' He straightened suddenly and looked down at her coldly. 'Ryan was a good man, but he was easily influenced. You will not find it quite so easy to get round me.'

Then he smiled lazily, his eyes flitting over her. 'I have nothing against sampling what you have to offer, but I warn you you will gain nothing in return.'

'I'm offering you nothing and I want nothing from you!' A flash of belated anger brought her back to her senses. Shiona sprang to her feet to confront him furiously. 'You think you can intimidate me, but you're mistaken! I'm not scared of you, Jake MacKay! If you think you can claim custody of Kirsty, you're wrong. You'd ruin her life, and I won't let you!'

'You're the one who'd ruin her life. And take my word for it, you'll never have her!'

'Oh, but you're wrong! I love my sister. And I'll fight for her, if need be! What sort of home could you possibly give her—even if you were suitable as a parent, anyway? Would you have her dragged up by a succession of au pairs and housekeepers while you went gallivanting all over the world? Is that the sort of future you intend to provide for her?'

'And what sort of future would you provide, surrounded by your glitzy London friends? A future of wild parties and extravagant spending?' Jake laughed a hollow laugh and regarded her flintily. 'Perhaps you're hoping she'll end up like you? Poor Kirsty. That's the worst thing anyone could wish on her.'

The insult hurt. It made her catch her breath. But with an effort Shiona forced herself to swallow it. 'What I can provide for Kirsty is security and love. Financially, I have the wherewithall to give her a very good life. And since I'm my own boss, my hours are flexible. I can work while she's at school, and be at home when she needs me.

'What's more, I intend to hire a live-in nanny to give me a hand and to be there when I can't. And there's a very good school near where I live. Don't worry, I'll see that she has everything she needs.'

She paused for a moment before pointedly adding, 'As to your other point, I must confess I think it would be worse if she ended up like you.' She spoke the words softly, but with feeling. 'Anyone who's prepared to use a child as a pawn just to score points in some personal vendetta has to be just about the lowest form of life. You *know* that Kirsty would be better off with me. You know I love her. You know I'd look after her.'

'What a hypocrite you are!' Jake's tone was lethal as he looked down at her with eyes that had turned to blue ice. 'When did you ever look after anyone except yourself? The only reason you want custody of Kirsty is so you can get your hands on her inheritance. You're the one who's playing games with an innocent child's future!'

'I'm doing nothing of the sort. I wouldn't dream of doing that!'

'That's just as well, for you'll get nothing out of her. Not a single penny, I assure you. For if I have my way, when this custody suit is over you'll never set eyes on Kirsty again.'

Shiona could see from his eyes that he meant it. She felt her cheeks pale just at the thought of it. But even as she looked back at him, hating him, loathing him, a new thought suddenly popped into her head.

With new confidence she looked back at him. 'I think you're fooling yourself. What court is going to award custody of a five-year-old girl to a single man who's constantly overseas on business? Especially when she happens to have a half-sister who can provide her with a stable and secure home in London?' She allowed herself a thin smile of triumph. 'I think you'll agree your case is pretty hopeless?'

He did not answer immediately. He stuffed his hands in his trouser-pockets and regarded her with enigmatic eyes. Then, to her surprise, he conceded, 'You're absolutely right. Put like that, my case does sound pretty hopeless.'

'I'd go so far as to say that you're wasting your time even to think of applying for custody.'

'Yes, it looks that way.' He glanced away for a moment, his gaze seeming to drift beyond the window to the loch and the granite peak of Ben Lomond beyond.

Shiona felt a shaft of sudden optimism. Perhaps he realised he'd been rash. Perhaps he wasn't going to fight her, after all.

But then he glanced back at her, and his expression had hardened. 'However, the situation is not quite as you've described it.'

Shiona felt herself tense. 'In what way?' she demanded.

'There is one small detail I have omitted to tell you, and that I feel will have a certain bearing on the judge's ruling.' He smiled a harsh smile and held her eyes as he told her, 'You may be able to offer Kirsty a comfortable single-parent home in London, but I can offer her a great deal more than that. . .'

'An ultra-luxurious single-parent home in Edinburgh, in which the parent is regularly absent?' Shiona threw him a hard look. 'You'll have to do better than that!'

Jake held her gaze. 'Then how about this. . .? What if I could offer her a proper home, a proper family, with *two* parents? What if I could offer her both a father and a mother?'

Shiona's stomach tightened. 'What are you saying?' She did not like the smile of relish that was suddenly creeping over his features.

'What I'm saying, my dear Shiona, is really very

simple. . .' Jake smiled sadistically as he prepared to drop his bombshell. 'What I'm saying is that I can provide something that you cannot—a proper family set-up for Kirsty to grow up in.

'You see, my very dear Shiona, I'm planning to get married in a couple of weeks' time.'

CHAPTER TWO

'MARRIED? *You*? In a couple of weeks' time?' Shiona gasped and blinked disbelievingly. 'You can't be serious! You're pulling my leg!'

'Absolutely not. I'm deadly serious. What's the matter? Did you think that no one would have me?'

Jake smiled as he said it, knowing perfectly well that no such thought had ever entered her head. After all, he was an eminently eligible man, attractive and immensely wealthy. There must be dozens of women who'd be only too happy to marry him.

She had dreamed of it herself once, Shiona thought with a painful flutter. But that was before she had taught herself to hate him.

'So, you see. . .' Jake was smiling down at her triumphantly '. . . I think you will agree this rather changes the situation. If you foolishly persist in pressing your claim for custody, you'll be wasting both your time and your money. And I know how much the latter means to you, my dear.'

For once, Shiona barely registered the insult. Her brain was spinning with the shock of his revelation. He was right, his getting married changed things dramatically. In any fight for Kirsty he would definitely have the edge.

She had a sudden dark suspicion that he was doing

this deliberately—cold-bloodedly engineering a convenient marriage just to do her out of custody. But
almost in the same instant she rejected that idea.
Surely no one, not even Jake, could be as calculating
as that?

'So aren't you going to congratulate me?' His tone
was taunting. 'Aren't you going to wish me every
happiness for the future?'

No, she damned well wasn't! Shiona eyed him
abrasively. 'Who is this woman you're planning to
marry? Do I know her? Have we ever met?'

'I'm afraid you haven't yet had that pleasure.' With
a smug smile, he reseated himself in his armchair
and, lifting his cup, took a swig of his tea. 'She's a
lovely person. She'll make an ideal wife—and a
perfect mother for Kirsty, of course.'

'You're sure about that?' Shiona remained standing. 'You're quite sure she's a fit person to be a
mother to my sister?'

'Oh, yes, my dear Shiona, I'm absolutely sure.
She'll be a far better mother than you're capable of
being.'

That hurt, but Shiona did not show it. 'You haven't
told me yet who she is.' Her expression was impen-
etrable as she faced him. 'Is there some secrecy
surrounding her identity, or does this fiancée of
yours have a name?'

He smiled right through her. 'There's no secrecy,
dear Shiona. Her name, since you're so curious, is
Janice.'

'And does she do anything in particular, this

Janice? Does she work? Does she have a career of some description?'

'Yes, she works. She's an executive secretary.'

'Yours?'

'Not quite, but she works with my firm.'

'How very convenient. Once you're married, you'll be able to have her at your beck and call twenty-four hours a day.' She smiled at him acidly. 'That should suit you right down to the ground.'

Jake smiled, quite unperturbed by her sarcasm, and helped himself to a shortbread biscuit. He took a bite. 'I'm afraid not. Once we're married, she'll be leaving the company. Janice plans to stay at home and devote herself to looking after me and Kirsty.'

'Don't jump the gun!' He was being just a bit too sure of himself. 'You haven't been awarded custody yet!'

'But I will be. You'll see.' He took another bite of his shortbread. 'Face it, Shiona, you haven't a hope.'

She had to admit it looked that way. What judge would award custody of a five-year-old girl to a single working woman down in London when there was a proper home, with both a father and a mother, waiting for her right here in the country of her birth?

With a little inner sigh Shiona turned to the window and gazed out thoughtfully at the loch. As much as she wanted Kirsty to be with her, she could see that she might be better off with Jake. And little Kirsty's welfare was the only thing that mattered.

She turned round slowly and looked Jake in the eye. 'If you can convince me that you can make Kirsty happy, believe me, I won't stand in your way.'

Then, as he raised surprised eyebrows, she added a warning. 'What I decide, however, depends on what I think of Janice. I have to be convinced that she'll make a good mother.'

'I already told you. . .' Cruel blue eyes looked straight back at her. 'She'll make a far, far better mother than you ever could.'

'That's your opinion.'

'It'll also be the judge's—if you're so foolish as to go ahead and fight me.' Jake sat back in his seat and surveyed her critically. 'What kind of mother could you possibly be when you're working all day and out partying all night? Looking after a child is a full-time job, not something to be slotted in when you have a spare moment.'

Out partying all night! That would have been comical if it hadn't been so downright offensive.

But Shiona kept her cool, though her tone was contemptuous as she responded. 'Lots of mothers these days manage to work and look after their children perfectly well. And I've already explained to you how I would arrange things.'

'Ah, yes, of course, the live-in nanny to look after her while you're out enjoying the high life.'

'What high life are you talking about?' She breathed deeply with irritation. 'I spend most of my evenings, as it happens, at home.'

Jake laughed out loud. 'Pull the other one! Don't tell me you've lost your taste for nightclubs and fancy restaurants.'

'I never had any particular taste for nightclubs and

fancy restaurants. That's a fable you invented all by yourself.'

'Lord, but you're good!' Jake shook his head scornfully. 'If I didn't know better, I might almost believe you.' Then, as she skewered him with a look of pure detestation, he reached out suddenly and caught her by the wrists. 'But I know all about you, remember! Beneath that wholesome, respectable façade you put up, I know what you're really like!'

'I doubt that very much!' Shiona wriggled to be free of him. 'You may think you do, but you know nothing about me!'

'I don't *think* I do, I *know* I do!' He rose to his feet to hold her more firmly. 'And you know exactly how I came to know—and how you influenced and finally ruined my brother!'

Shiona felt her control desert her for a moment. 'How can you believe that?' Her heart twisted inside her. 'All I ever did was try to help Ryan.'

'You mean help yourself!' Jake would never believe her. His eyes were like splinters as he glowered down at her, yet in their depths she could see the pain that tormented him.

He had loved his younger brother with a fierce, protective love capable of showing no mercy to those who sought to harm him. That was why she knew he would always hate her. He believed she had brought about Ryan's downfall.

He shook her roughly. 'Ryan trusted you. He loved you, for pity's sake! How could you do what you did to him?'

His pain and anger were like a lance twisting

through her. Shiona could scarcely bear to look at him. And there was nothing she could say in her own defence. Her promise to Ryan had sealed her lips forever.

Almost to herself she murmured, 'I loved him, too. I promise you it wasn't like you think.'

But Jake wasn't listening. He wasn't interested in her denials. His eyes were hard as he tightened his grip on her.

'So, you see, I don't intend to let history repeat itself. There's no way I'll let you get your hands on Kirsty.' He narrowed his eyes at her. 'Don't waste your time here. Just pack your bags and get on back to London.'

'I'll pack my bags when I'm good and ready——' Shiona eyed him defiantly '—and not a moment before!'

'But you're wasting your time. You have nothing to stay for!'

'That may be, but I'll decide when I leave!'

'Unless, of course——' Jake's eyes glittered down at her. 'Unless your reason for hanging around here is simply to irritate me with your unwelcome presence.' As she tried to tug her hands free, he jerked her closer, so that her body was pressed against his. 'Is that what's behind this stubbornness of yours?'

'Don't be so stupid! Just let me go!' Shiona writhed against him as he simply held her tighter.

'First, answer my question,' he insisted. 'Do you secretly enjoy getting in my hair?'

She looked up into his face, anger seething through her, and was surprised to see that he was smiling.

Then as his hand released her wrist and slid round against her back, drawing her even closer so that the warmth of him burned through her, something very strange suddenly happened inside her.

In an instant the coldness of her fury evaporated and her heart was flooded with a tide of raw emotions—excitement, confusion and a desperate yearning that tore at her insides and left her breathless, as though she had been knocked to the ground and run over by a steam train.

Shiona struggled for breath, appalled that she should react like this. Surely all these emotions had died long ago?

'Answer me, my little temptress.' His eyes burned into her, so blue, like sapphires, and twice as brilliant. And the scent of him in her nostrils was dark and heady. 'You know the battle's already lost,' he was saying. 'There can be no other reason for wanting to stay on here.'

With an effort she struggled to the surface of the emotions that, like a bubbling maelstrom, threatened to pull her under. And, somehow, in a frail voice, she managed to tell him, 'The battle's not over. That's why I'm staying.'

'In that case, the next few weeks should be interesting.' The hand on her back had crept up to her neck, sending squiggles of sensation from her scalp to her toes. 'In fact, I reckon they should be very interesting indeed.'

'And why should they be interesting?' That was not a word she would have chosen. 'Fraught' and 'unpleasant' sprang more readily to mind.

'They will allow me to have a taste of what Ryan had the privilege of enjoying—albeit,' he added, smiling, 'with certain restrictions. I am, after all, soon to be married.'

He was talking in riddles. 'Restrictions? What restrictions?'

Jake laughed then. 'You're right. What need is there for restrictions? While I am still free, I am at liberty to take my pleasure when I choose. And you are, after all, such an irresistible little temptress.'

All at once Shiona didn't like the look in his eyes. The warmth of a moment ago that had so overwhelmed her had cooled to a more familiar glint of contempt. She tried to pull away from him. 'What the devil are you talking about? Let me go and kindly stop talking in riddles!'

He did not let her go, but his grip on her slackened. He took a step away and looked down into her face. 'For the next couple of weeks it looks as though we'll be living together. That is, if you seriously intend to stay on.'

'I most certainly do intend to stay on!' Shiona's hazel eyes flickered with resolve. 'But what makes you think we'll be living together? Your home is in Edinburgh, not here.'

'My home is where I choose.' Unexpectedly, he released her. 'And right now I choose to make my home here. Until the final custody proceedings are over, it is best for Kirsty that she remain here, where her friends are, where she feels most at home.'

Shiona couldn't have agreed more, but all the same

she felt her heart sink. 'But it's not necessary for you to be here if I'm here,' she protested.

She might have guessed at his answer. 'I would say it's *doubly* necessary. As we have already discussed, I don't want you influencing her. As it is, you've already had her to yourself for too long during my regrettable but unavoidable absence. I left her in the care of Nettie and Inge. I had no idea that you'd be coming here to spin your little web.'

Shiona felt like striking him. The man was intolerable. 'Kirsty's my sister,' she reminded him in a sharp tone. 'And if you have any intention of trying to keep her from me, I warn you, I won't stand for it!'

'And how will you stop me?' Jake regarded her arrogantly.

'I'll stop you. Don't worry.' Her eyes flashed a warning. 'That is something you can be very sure of.'

To her irritation, he smiled. 'Quite the little tiger, aren't you? I shall quite enjoy taming you over the next couple of weeks.' He reached out to cup her chin with his fingers. 'Yes, I think I shall enjoy that very much indeed.'

Her temper suddenly snapping, Shiona slapped his hand away. 'God, I hate you, Jake MacKay! You're the most contemptible individual I've ever encountered in my life!'

'So, at least we have something in common,' he countered. His eyes blazed through her, as though they would consume her. 'It has long been my opinion that you, my dear Shiona, are the most contemptible individual that *I* have ever encountered.'

He smiled a twisted smile. 'Two such contemptible individuals ought to prove an excellent match for one another. The more I think about it, I must say, the more I'm looking forward to our time together.'

That did not surprise her. Jake thrived on conflict. There was no one who enjoyed throwing his weight around more.

Shiona raised her head scornfully, about to voice that very notion, but at that very moment the sitting-room door burst open and a small excited figure burst into the room.

'Aunt Shiona! Aunt Shiona!' With a squeal of delight, Kirsty rushed into her arms.

Shiona held her for a moment, her anger instantly vanishing to be replaced by a warm, maternal well of love. Then, carefully stifling her own personal feelings, she took the little girl by the hand. 'Look who's come to see you. Uncle Jake. Aren't you going to say hello to him?'

'Uncle Jake! I didn't see you!' With another whoop of delight the child threw herself at Jake, flinging her arms around him as he bent down to scoop her up.

Shiona felt her heart tug as she watched them together, aware as always of how very alike they were. The same almost black hair, the same vivid blue eyes. There was no doubt that Kirsty was one hundred per cent MacKay.

She cleared her throat. 'Did you have a good day at school?'

The little girl turned round, nodding enthusiastically. 'We had sums, and I came top of the class!'

'Clever girl!' Jake ruffled her hair and kissed her. 'I think you deserve a treat for that.'

'What kind of treat?' The child's eyes widened. 'Can I have it now, Uncle Jake?'

'Of course you can. It's out in the car. Come on and help me look for it.'

As he set her on the floor again, Kirsty turned to Shiona. 'You come, too. Come and look for my treat.' Then she was bounding out of the room, heading for the front door and rushing outside into the garden.

Without a glance at one another the two adults followed, Jake stepping aside at the sitting-room door to allow Shiona to pass into the hall ahead of him. And in that instant he paused to look into her face, causing her to glance up automatically at him.

'She's a delightful child, isn't she?' he observed. Then, as Shiona nodded, he added a malicious warning. 'I would advise you to enjoy her while you can. You may not have very much longer.'

That night Shiona lay in bed, propped up against the pillows, trying to read. She had known she wouldn't sleep. Her brain was teeming with a whole tangle of emotions that she could barely sort out.

The remainder of the day had passed almost enjoyably, with Jake and Shiona and little Kirsty appearing to behave like a happy little family. For in the presence of Kirsty Jake behaved impeccably, with not the slightest hint of animosity towards Shiona, just as Shiona behaved towards him.

Yet Shiona could not quite drive his warning from her mind and the look of cold dislike that had accompanied it. She would never grow used to the way he hated her.

But on the surface, at least, all was sweetness and light, and there was no doubt that his affection for Kirsty was genuine. Shiona smiled to herself with an uneasy kind of pleasure. He might be all the rotters of the universe, but he had a gentle, magical touch with the child.

And it was equally obvious that Kirsty adored him. She seemed to beam with happiness in his presence and hang on every word he said.

Shiona sighed and leaned back against the pillows. How painfully that reminded her of herself.

Once, she, too, had hung on his every word and beamed with happiness just at the sight of him. Once, she had worshipped the ground he walked on. Once, she would have died just to hear a kind word.

Shiona had been sixteen when Jake entered her life. Innocent. Impressionable. Hopelessly unworldly. A beautiful child full of wild ambitions and a passion to taste all the good things in life. And Jake, at twenty-four, dark and dashing and handsome, had appeared to embody all the romance that she dreamed of. Her heart had been lost to him the first moment she had set eyes on him.

That first meeting had been shortly after she and her mother had moved into the house on the banks of Loch Lomond, and even now she remembered it as a magical time.

The house alone had been like a dream come true after the two-bedroomed flat on the outskirts of Stirling where she and her mother had lived in near penury for the past seven years since Shiona's father's death.

'So, how do you like it? Does it meet with your approval?'

She remembered how Douglas, her new step-father, had taken pleasure in showing her round Lomond View, pointing out the paintings, the antiques, the porcelain, the like of which she had never seen before.

'I think it's all gorgeous!' she had enthused with real feeling. 'It's the most wonderful place that anyone could live!'

He had ruffled her hair. 'I'm glad to hear you say that, because from now on this is your home.'

Shiona had looked into his face with a stab of emotion, and just for a moment had been unable to speak. This man, whom she had taken to immediately, had transformed the lives of herself and her mother.

Her mother had shed ten years since her marriage to Douglas, and after all the years of struggle had learned to laugh again. And Douglas had promised that Shiona's lifelong ambition—to study fashion design in London—was hers for the taking if she could make the grade. No longer would it be necessary for her to leave school early and find a job to help support the household. Thanks to Douglas, her future was rosy.

At last she had found her voice and managed to

tell him, 'Thank you. Thank you for everything, Douglas.'

'Don't be silly. It's my pleasure.' He had fished in the pocket of his grey wool cardigan and, with a broad smile, produced a small jeweller's box. He'd handed it to Shiona. 'This is for you. A little gift to welcome you to Lomond View.'

'You shouldn't, really. . .'

But he'd simply laughed at her protestations, the same way he always laughed when her mother protested at his seemingly endless generosity. 'Open it up. See if you like it.'

Shiona had opened the box and her heart leapt within her. 'It's absolutely beautiful! Oh, thank you, Douglas!'

'Put it on. Here, let me help you.' He had lifted the locket on its fine gold chain and deftly fastened it around her neck. Then he'd turned her round to admire her. 'You look terrific. Let's go downstairs and show it off to the others.'

Shiona would never forget the next few minutes when the two of them had arrived in the big sunny sitting-room.

Ryan had instantly jumped to his feet, beaming at her as he crossed the room towards her. 'It's the locket we saw in town the other day! The one in the window, the one you so admired!' He'd grinned from ear to ear, grey eyes dancing. 'It suits you perfectly. You couldn't have chosen better.'

'Thanks. I love it.' Shiona had smiled back at the fair-haired youth who had so recently become her brother. Already she had become exceedingly fond of him. Ryan had been as warm and as welcoming as his father.

And then, quite suddenly, over Ryan's shoulder, she had been aware of a tall dark figure watching her.

Ryan had seen her gaze shift. 'Let me introduce you. This is Jake, the big brother I'm forever telling you about.'

With barely a smile Jake had then stepped forward, and Shiona had felt her heart clench anxiously inside her as a pair of blue eyes, as bright as sapphires, just for a moment had seemed to pierce through her.

He'd held out his hand to her. 'Pleased to meet you.' And as his fingers clasped hers, a strange sensation had shot through her, as though with that handshake he had branded her forever. For she had known in that instant that this dark-haired man before her was destined to leave his mark on her soul.

'Pleased to meet you,' she had responded, for the very first time since her arrival at Loch Lomond feeling unaccountably awkward and strange.

With a veiled smile he had glanced down at the locket. 'My brother's right. You chose very well.'

Looking back on that moment, it had often occurred to Shiona that it had marked the path that their future relationship was to take. For in the softly spoken comment she had sensed condemnation. She had sensed that he believed she had asked for the locket, that she was guilty of abusing his father's generosity.

Perhaps she should have put him right there and

then, but at the time it had not seemed terribly important, for instantly, chameleon-like, his demeanour had altered. In the flicker of an eyelid the hostility had vanished and he had become a model of charm and smiling good humour, as he politely asked her all about herself and answered her questions in return. At the end of the day Shiona had innocently believed that her second new stepbrother was her friend.

That misconception had continued on and off over the following six or seven years. Six or seven years in the course of which her infatuation with him, in spite of the rare times she saw him, had grown increasingly severe.

It was that detached, aloof quality of his, she had often thought, that had originally attracted her so fatally to him. That strength of mind one could sense below the surface, that glow of authority that seemed to radiate from his skin.

'He's like our father,' Ryan had once told her. 'Not only in looks, but in character, too.'

And though Douglas on the surface was more generous, more giving than his sometimes taciturn elder son, Shiona recognised that what they shared in common was that fierce individuality and sense of purpose that had brought Douglas, through his own efforts, from rags to great riches. Jake, she had sensed, would be capable of the same.

'Me, I'm like our mother,' Ryan had gone on to enlighten her. 'You've seen photographs of our mother, haven't you?'

Shiona had nodded. 'She was very beautiful. And you are just like her, with the same blond hair.'

Certainly, two brothers could scarcely have been more different—and not only in looks, in temperament as well. Younger by four years than his go-getting elder brother, Ryan was basically easygoing, with no driving ambitions, content just to get by. Jake, by contrast, quite independently of his father, who had also made his fortune in the building industry, had set up as a building contractor on his own. And already, at twenty-four, he'd built up a formidable business, successfully fulfilling contracts all over the world.

'When our father retires, he'll take over his business, too. No wonder Dad's proud of him,' Ryan had told her.

'But what about you? Wouldn't you like to be a part of it?' Shiona had felt obliged to ask him.

He had shaken his head. 'That's not for me. And, anyway, how could I compete with a brother like Jake?'

Shiona sank against the pillows now and closed her eyes as a rush of sadness went washing through her. Poor Ryan, he had had a heart of gold. It was a tragedy that he should have died so young.

She bit her lip, remembering that awful time when the news had come that he had lost his life in the fire that had demolished his holiday hotel—and how the tragedy, for her, had turned into a nightmare. For it had been when Ryan had died, three years ago now, that the situation between her and Jake had come to a head.

The disapproval she had sometimes sensed from him, and that had bothered her fleetingly from time to time, had erupted into a torrent of burning hatred at the discovery that, in spite of the fortune his father had showered on him, Ryan had died in a state of virtual penury. To Shiona's absolute horror, Jake had blamed her.

Everyone knew she and Ryan had been living together, and it was easy to jump to the wrong conclusions. But things had not been at all what they'd seemed—though she was bound by her promise never to reveal the truth.

She'd paid bitterly and dearly for her unshakeable loyalty. For since that day when he had made his accusations, tearing her heart to shreds in the process, Jake had refused to have any more to do with her. For three years they had neither met nor spoken. The rift had been total and, she had believed, final.

At first the agony had been unbearable. She had loved him, almost obsessively, since the age of sixteen and, though he had never in any way encouraged her, over the years she had built all her dreams around him. He was the man she had prayed that one day she would marry. And now, to this man, she had ceased to exist.

But she had turned her agony into a blessing. Recognising the hopelessness of her situation, she had resolved to do what she ought to have done years ago, and systematically banished him from her heart.

It had not been easy, but she had succeeded—principally by concentrating on her career. Three years ago she had just recently left college, one of thousands of graduates looking for a job. Now she was running her own knitwear business with a design studio in London and a busy workshop here in Scotland. She'd had to work like a Trojan to achieve it, but it had been worth every drop of blood, sweat and tears.

And not only for the pleasure of running her own thriving business, but for the more fundamental change it had brought about in her. That impressionable child who had swooned and sighed and lain in bed dreaming of Jake MacKay had finally grown up with a vengeance. Her days of swooning and sighing were over. Professional success had knocked some sense into her, and she had taught herself to return hate with hate.

Furthermore, she had grown to be grateful for the fact that their lives had drifted irretrievably apart, and she had prayed that things might stay that way for ever. But now the tragedy that had killed her mother and Jake's father and made an orphan of little Kirsty had, cruelly, brought them together again.

She leaned back against the pillows and, sighing, closed her eyes. She had thought she was healed, beyond his reach forever, and in every real sense she knew that she was. But today she had felt old wounds being ripped open. Even as she lay there, she could feel them ache and throb.

She sighed again, and switched off the light and dropped her unread book on to the floor. But there was one thing she was sure of. He could torture her all he wanted, but he would not succeed in breaking her a second time.

Beneath the sheets she clenched her fists. She would die before she would let him do that.

CHAPTER THREE

'So, YOU'RE still here, are you? I thought you might have gone.'

Shiona glanced round, startled out of her reverie, as Jake appeared suddenly in the doorway of the breakfast-room. 'Of course I'm still here. Where else would I be?'

'When you didn't show up to see Kirsty off to school this morning, I thought you might have caught an early flight back to London.' He walked into the room, his eyes travelling over her, disapproval in every harsh line of his face. 'However, I see that you've only just got up.'

Seated at the breakfast table in her pink wool robe, Shiona felt a blush rise to her cheeks. It was after ten o'clock, and he would be quite right to disapprove, if it weren't for the fact that, in spite of appearances, she had slept for only a few hours last night. She'd heard the grandfather clock down in the hall chime every quarter-hour until three o'clock. No wonder she hadn't wakened till after half-past nine!

But she wasn't about to excuse herself to Jake. 'It's Inge's job to see Kirsty off to school.' Defiantly, Shiona tilted her chin at him. 'It really wasn't necessary for me to be here too.'

'That's what I thought you'd say. Leave it to the au pair. Let someone else look after your sister while you have a few hours' extra beauty sleep.' He came to stand before her. 'You don't change, do you? Still looking after number one, as ever.'

As his eyes, blue and flinty, held hers, Shiona was tempted to protest that that wasn't fair. Every morning since she'd been here, apart from today, she'd been up bright and early to see Kirsty off to school.

But she didn't say it. She didn't care what Jake thought of her. He already hated her, so what difference did it make?

'Still, never mind.' He drew back one of the chairs and proceeded to seat himself at the table opposite her. 'Your absence meant that I had her all to myself at breakfast—with the additional pleasure of escorting her personally to school.'

Shiona ignored his smug smile. 'How dutiful on your part. You're really putting on quite an impressive little show. I wonder how many times in the past, when you've been staying here, you've gone to the trouble of escorting Kirsty to school?'

His gaze never flickered. 'I'd say at least a dozen.'

It was probably true, but she responded scornfully, just as he always did to her. 'Sure,' she scoffed. 'I'll just bet you have!'

'Ask Kirsty, if you doubt it.' He regarded her smoothly. 'Believe me, I wouldn't go to the trouble of lying to you.'

Had he emphasised the 'you', implying that she wasn't worth lying to, or had she simply imagined the insult? Shiona looked back at him, hiding the flicker of hurt inside her. 'I think you'd lie to St

Peter,' she retorted evenly, 'if you thought you might get something out of it.'

He merely smiled. 'I think, my dear Shiona, you've rather got that the wrong way round. *You're* the opportunist around here, not me.'

'Of course. I was forgetting.' Shiona smiled at him sarcastically. 'And you're the one with a halo around his head!'

The blue eyes surveyed her face for a moment, their expression dark and oddly unreadable. Then, with a shrug, he let his gaze slide over to the coffee-pot. 'Is there any coffee left?' he enquired.

'I'm not sure. I think there ought to be.'

She was on the point of reaching over to pick up the coffee-pot and obligingly fill one of the spare cups for him. But, just in time, she managed to stop herself. She had reacted out of habit. It had been a kind of reflex action. But she wasn't Jake's little slave girl any more.

Deliberately, she pushed her hands into the pockets of her robe and sat back in her chair as he proceeded to serve himself. Once, she would not only have poured his coffee for him, she would have spooned in the sugar and stirred it for him, too. Then sat and gazed at him adoringly while he drank.

She felt a clench in her stomach of resentment and rage as she remembered just how pathetically servile she had once been. In those bad old days she would even shine his shoes for him, and beg for the privilege of hosing down his car. And he, of course, would accept her ministrations as though they were quite simply no more than his due.

Suddenly she felt deeply irritated by his presence. 'What are you doing here anyway at this hour of the day?' Her tone was barbed, unmistakably hostile. 'Shouldn't you be at your desk in Edinburgh, sorting out the world?'

He deliberately took a mouthful of his coffee before answering. 'Is that where you would like me to be, Shiona?'

She met his eyes. 'That wouldn't be my first choice. Personally, I'd choose somewhere a little further away.' Like Outer Mongolia, she added to herself, as she lifted up her own cup and drank. Then, as he simply smiled, she regarded him over the top of it. 'I thought you were a workaholic? I thought Jake MacKay Contracting couldn't operate without you?'

'What a flattering notion. So, you believe me indispensable? I had no idea you held me in such high regard.'

'Oh, believe me, I don't,' Shiona assured him quickly, irritated at herself for handing him that one on a plate. 'It's just that I know how all-controlling you are. How can you bear to relinquish the helm, even for a single minute?'

'And who says I have relinquished the helm?' Jake regarded her with superior amusement. 'If there are any important decisions to be made, I'm only a telephone call away.'

'Ah, but when the cat's away the mice will play. Someone might do something behind your back.'

'You're right.' He smiled a mirthless smile. 'And that's precisely why I'm here. The only one I'm worried about doing things behind my back, my dear

Shiona, is your sweet self.' As she glared at him, he continued, 'So get used to the fact that, if you plan on staying on here, you will unfortunately be seeing rather a lot of me. There's no way I intend leaving you alone here with Kirsty.'

Damn him! Shiona glowered across the table at him—so utterly poised, so hatefully sure of himself in his immaculate dark blue Savile Row suit. As always, he had that look of having the world on a string, everything indisputably under his control.

Shiona scowled into his face with its arrogant high cheekbones, self-satisfied mouth and eyes as hard as sapphires. How hateful he was. How could she ever have loved him?

She laid down her cup and leaned towards him across the table. 'And what exactly do you think I might do to Kirsty if you were rash enough to leave her alone with me?' She bit the words out at him, full of anger and resentment. 'You're not seriously suggesting I might do her some harm?'

'Not physical harm.'

'Then what kind of harm?'

'Emotional. Moral. Psychological. Who knows?'

'That's cruel and unfair! How can you say it?'

'Because I've learned from bitter experience precisely what you're capable of. I've told you that already. Why do you keep insisting?'

He was referring to Ryan again. She could see it in his eyes. That flicker of pain and anger that would never go away. And again she felt that helpless rush inside her, knowing that she would never be able to set the record straight.

She turned her eyes away, unable to answer him. It really did still hurt that he believed her capable of such evil. She had a feeling it probably always would. Without looking at him, she listened as Jake went on to say,

'I hate to keep repeating myself, but you really are wasting your time. Why don't you just give up and go back down to London? It can't be so easy for *you* to run your business from here.'

'I'll manage, thank you.' Her tone was curt. It was no affair of his that she had left the London studio in the capable hands of her assistant. It would tick over perfectly without her for a few weeks. She flicked Jake an openly sarcastic smile. 'There's really no need for you to be concerned.'

There was a momentary silence as she averted her gaze again, and she was aware of him picking up his coffee-cup and drinking.

Then he said conversationally, laying down his cup again, 'I hear your business is doing very well.'

'Is that what you hear?' Still she did not look at him.

'My congratulations. You've done very well. I hear you were even nominated for the Young Designer of the Year Award.'

There he went again, playing the good guy, pretending he was interested in her success! But she would not stand for his condescension. Shiona twisted round and pierced him with a look. 'No doubt that surprised you, even irritated you a little. I bet it really gets up your nose that my knitwear's proving so popular.'

'Why should you believe that?' One straight black eyebrow lifted. 'Why should I be anything but pleased at your success?'

Because you hate me! Because you despise me! Because you'd like to see me suffer for what you believe I did to Ryan!

How she would have loved to have yelled these words at him and finally have the whole thing out in the open. But she could not, so she simply told him in a flat tone, 'We've recently started exporting to Europe and Japan. I've had to take on more staff at the workshop in Killearn.'

'Again my congratulations.'

He was so damned convincing!

'You must have put in a lot of hard work.'

Of course, the irony of what he had just said escaped him, but it caused Shiona to smile a bitter inner smile. Often she had wondered if she would have been quite so successful if she hadn't thrown herself so totally into her work in a desperate attempt to mend her broken heart. Perhaps, to some extent, she thought with wry amusement, she owed her professional success to Jake.

She glanced across at him. 'Yes, it's been a lot of hard work. But, fortunately, hard work is something I enjoy.'

'Not all hard work, I hope?' He threw her a strange smile. 'I hope you've had time for other things as well?'

'Other things?' She feigned incomprehension. 'What sorts of other things do you mean?'

'The normal sorts of things that make up one's life.
Friends. . .leisure interests. . . Hobbies, if you like.'

'You mean parties and fast living? Isn't that more
my line?' Shiona regarded him harshly, tossing back
her auburn hair. 'I admit I've had to cut back a little
just recently, but I'm hoping to get back into my
stride really soon.'

Jake shook his head as he continued to watch her,
regarding her irritated face with a discreetly shuttered look. 'No doubt you are, but that's not what I
was meaning. What I was wondering was if you have
any serious boyfriend these days?'

'Serious boyfriend? I don't go in for serious boyfriends. I only take up with men for what I can get
out of them.' Her hazel eyes glinted across the table
at him. 'But surely you, of all people, don't need to
be told that?'

Suddenly she was shimmering with anger as she
faced him, yet not quite certain where her anger had
sprung from. His conversation, though insincere,
had not been unpleasant. She was the one who had
initiated this skirmish.

She could see in his eyes that he was thinking the
same, as in a flat tone he told her, 'Point taken. Let's
drop the subject.'

But still her anger continued to bubble as a new
suspicion came into her mind. 'What's the matter?
Were you worried that I might be on the verge of
getting married, too? Was that why you wanted to
pry into my private life? After all, if I did have a
fiancé tucked away, that would change the situation

rather dramatically. I'd have as strong a claim for custody as you!'

'Indeed you would. But, take my word for it, the possibility had never for one moment occurred to me.'

Had it not, indeed? That was vaguely insulting.

But before she could react, Jake went on to assure her, 'What's more, you're wrong to believe I was prying. All I was doing was making conversation. I couldn't be less interested in your private life, as it happens.'

Another fleeting insult. Shiona straightened her shoulders, feeling jumpy and hopelessly out of control. 'That's just as well,' she told him evenly, 'because I don't intend discussing it with you.' Then she rose to her feet—she'd had enough of this conversation. 'If you don't mind, I think I'll go and get dressed.'

'I don't mind in the least.' He glanced at his watch. 'I'll be going to collect Kirsty from school in about an hour. If you like. . .'

He paused just long enough for her to wonder if he was about to do the decent thing and invite her to join him. Then he smiled into her face as he finished the sentence.

'If you like, I can drop you off at the travel agent's so that you can book your flight back down to London.'

Shiona eyed him coldly. 'That won't be necessary. I'll be booking my ticket when I'm ready.' Then she tilted her chin at him. 'However, I will come with you. I'd like to go and collect Kirsty, too.'

Jake simply smiled. 'You may as well while you

can. As I warned you already, you may not have very much longer.' Then, as Shiona started to turn away, her body stiff with loathing, he added calmly, 'Oh, by the way, I have a piece of news that I think will interest you. . .'

She half turned round. 'Yes? What is it?'

'You said you wanted to meet my fiancée so that you could judge her for yourself. Well, I'm happy to say, you'll soon have that opportunity. . .'

A smug smile curled around his lips. 'I've invited Janice to spend the weekend with us.'

Good. I'm glad the woman's coming. Shiona told herself with just a flicker of uncertainty, changing into second gear as she rounded a bend. It was important that she meet this fiancée as soon as possible, so that she could judge her suitability as a mother for Kirsty.

With a sigh now she took a turning off the narrow road into one of the summer picnic spots overlooking Loch Lomond. She drew the car to a halt and pulled on the handbrake. Once she'd met Janice and come to some conclusion, then she would know what she had to do next.

She stared at the still blue waters of the loch, overhung by weeping willows in their fresh spring greenery. A curlew called out as it rose above the waters, then came to rest alongside its mate among the rushes. Very likely there was a nest there, full of hungry little mouths waiting to be fed.

With another wistful sigh she sat back in her seat. More than anything she would love to be Kirsty's guardian and, in spite of the harsh things Jake had said to her, she knew, if that happened, she would do a good job.

But she also knew that if Jake and Janice could offer the happy home that Jake had promised she would give up her own claim in an instant. Though it would be a great personal sadness to have to do it, it would nevertheless give her the greatest satisfaction to see Kirsty settled in a warm and loving family. Having known the lack of that luxury herself, she was all too aware of how important it was.

She pursed her lips. Before the weekend was out she would know whether she should stay or go back to London. For her decision depended solely on her assessment of Janice.

As far as Jake was concerned, she had no doubts at all as to his suitability as a father. Sure, she had indulged in the occasional uncharitable observation that his affection for the child was no more than a front. But that didn't reflect her true opinion. It was merely an expression of her own personal dislike.

Jake loved Kirsty dearly. That was obvious to anyone. He seemed to love her as fiercely as he had once loved Ryan, Shiona thought to herself with a little inner shiver. And he had the makings of a strong, but kind and loving father, who would always have the little girl's best interests at heart.

But that wasn't enough, she reminded herself sharply, watching the male curlew as it waded out into the shallows, searching for food beneath the surface of the loch. Jake would be a good father when

he was around. But he was away a lot, and then it
would be up to Janice.

Janice. Just to think of her made Shiona anxious.
Kirsty's entire happiness could depend on Janice.

There were other feelings, too, that the thought of
Janice provoked. A sense of irritation. A sense of
resentment. A sense that she had no right to intrude
into their lives.

Ridiculous feelings, Shiona decided, rejecting
them. It was perfectly natural that Jake should
marry—and, apart from how it might affect Kirsty, it
was not an event that interested her in the slightest.

Though she had found one small revelation of mild
interest.

She and Jake had been driving back to Lomond
View after accompanying Kirsty back to school when
Jake had swivelled round in his seat to inform her,

'I've asked Nettie to prepare the rose room for
Janice—that is, if you have no objections. . . You
weren't planning to use it for any of your own guests,
were you?'

Shiona had shaken her head. 'No, I wasn't.' And
though she was not surprised that, for the sake of
appearances, Jake's fiancée was to be installed in one
of the guest-rooms, it did surprise her that he had
chosen the rose room. It was the guest-room that
was furthest away from his own room. He evidently
wasn't planning any passionate trysts!

She'd had no time to examine her reaction to this
revelation any further, however, for he had proceeded to cut across her thoughts.

'I understand you've never had a guest while

you've been here? You really ought to invite one of your boyfriends. I assure you I wouldn't mind in the least.'

It wasn't his place to mind, she'd felt like telling him. The house was as much hers as it was his. But she'd restricted herself to snapping, 'I'll bear that in mind,' and abruptly ending the conversation. For some reason his observation had niggled.

Now, a couple of soothing hours later—she'd spent most of that time at the Killearn workshop— she knew exactly why she'd reacted as she had. And why she'd reacted the same way yesterday evening when Jake had started questioning her about her private life.

On the subject of boyfriends Shiona was notoriously sensitive, and doubly so, it appeared, when Jake brought up the subject.

The curlew was still moving silently through the water, long, curved beak poised above the surface. Shiona watched it, reflecting that the reason for her sensitivity was that her private life was the only area of her existence that gave her absolutely no satisfaction at all. It remained empty, barren, a hopeless wasteland. Since that day when she had ruthlessly cut Jake from her heart there had been no one. No one who really mattered.

It wasn't that she hadn't tried to form relationships, but somehow they had just never amounted to anything significant.

'I don't think you really want a proper relationship,' one of her more recent boyfriends had told her. 'I don't think you're really interested in getting seriously involved.'

She'd tried to make a joke out of it. 'I'm just a slow starter! Don't worry, I'll get round to it eventually.' But in her heart she had felt a pang of unease. Was there something wrong with her that she seemed to shy away from commitment? After all, she was twenty-six years old. Why couldn't she, like other people, just fall in love?

Of course she *had* been in love, for years and years, and perhaps, she sometimes wondered, that experience had spoiled her. Perhaps all those years wasted mooning over Jake had somehow robbed her of the ability to give her love to someone more deserving.

For there had been no lack of men whom she had wished she could fall in love with, good men who would undoubtedly have made her happy. But, frustratingly, that vital spark had been missing.

Damn Jake! she thought for the hundred-millionth time. Damn him for ever coming into my life! And damn him for daring to pry into my affairs and for subtly mocking my singular state!

It was he who had tainted her! It was he who was to blame! He was a scourge on her life! How she hated him!

Shiona gripped the steering-wheel and squeezed her eyes shut and slowly counted up to ten. She was over-reacting. All this emotion was out of place. She had stopped giving a damn about Jake years ago.

She breathed in slowly, concentrating hard. It seemed that just being around him was starting to get to her. She bit her lip. She must be stronger than that.

She counted to ten, then opened her eyes again— to see the curlew suddenly emerge from the water with a fat, squirming fish held firmly in his beak.

Shiona smiled to herself. She must be like the curlew, and concentrate all her energy on those who needed her. She must think only of Kirsty and Kirsty's future. She must not think of Jake. Jake was the past.

She switched on the engine and headed back on to the road. The first part was easy. It was the second part that was hard.

'When are Uncle Jake and his friend Janice coming?' Kirsty was pressed against the drawing-room window, excitedly waiting for Jake's Mercedes to appear.

Shiona was seated on the sofa, her back to the window, leafing stiffly through a magazine. She glanced at her watch. 'Any minute now. If the train was on time, they should just about be here.'

'Here they are now! I can see the car!' With a whoop of pleasure Kirsty rushed across the room, heading for the door that led out into the hall. 'Come on, Aunt Shiona! Let's go and meet them!'

Shiona laid down her magazine. 'No, I'll wait here,' she smiled. 'You go and meet them, if you like.' Then she rose to her feet, as Kirsty scampered out i4to the hall, and, adjusting the collar of her cream silk blouse, walked on measured steps towards the window.

She stopped a few feet away, so that she was hidden by the curtains, and fixed her gaze unblinkingly on the long black Mercedes that was heading sedately up the driveway. She pushed back her hair, as bright as copper in the sunshine that slanted through the big bay window. This was it. The moment she'd been waiting for.

She breathed in deeply, seeking to allay her nervousness, eyes squinting impatiently to distinguish some shadow behind the infuriating smoked glass windows. What would she be like? Would she like her?

The car drew to a halt alongside the front door, and an instant later the driver's door swung open. Jake jumped out and strode round to the passenger door, but before he could open it Kirsty appeared, flinging herself at him and squealing, 'Uncle Jake! Uncle Jake!'

He paused to hug her and ruffle her hair, then at last the passenger door was swinging open and there was what seemed to Shiona an endless moment before Janice at last stepped into view.

Shiona stopped breathing, her heart pounding inside her. She looks all right, she assured herself warily. A little older and somewhat plainer than she'd expected, but the woman had a distinctly motherly look!

She felt elation and sadness all in the same instant. It looked as though she would lose Kirsty, after all. But how wonderful if this woman could give Kirsty a good home!

A moment later she had the opportunity for a

closer look, as the trio came trooping into the sitting-room, Jake in front, the two females right behind.

'Now meet Shiona,' Jake was saying, guiding his fiancée forwards with a hand at her waist. 'Shiona Fergusson, my stepsister.'

The smiling figure in the tan checked suit stepped forward with hand extended to greet her. 'Shiona, I'm delighted. I'm Janice MacGregor.' She shook hands warmly. 'I've heard so much about you.'

Shiona smiled back. 'Pleased to meet you, too.' And she was trying desperately not to be too obvious as her eyes scrutinised every line of the other woman's face.

Luckily, Janice had already glanced away, her eyes circling with interest the splendid sitting-room. And for an instant her expression seemed to alter subtly. A fleeting, hard look seemed to drift across her eyes. Almost as though, Shiona thought with a small shudder, she was mentally totting up the value of the contents of the room. But then an instant later she was wondering if she'd imagined it, as Janice turned to beam a warm, glowing smile at Jake.

'What a beautiful room! And what a splendid view you have! I had no idea it was so lovely here!'

Of course she'd imagined it, Shiona told herself firmly. Janice MacGregor was a perfectly nice person, and she, Shiona, in her hyped-up state, was simply looking for things to criticise.

'I'm glad you like it,' Jake was saying. 'You have almost as good a view from your bedroom.' He had stepped towards her, his hand on her waist again.

'I'll show it to you now. You can freshen up and change.'

'What a wonderful idea!' Janice beamed at him and slipped an arm through his before turning to Shiona. 'I hope you'll excuse me,' she apologised, smiling, 'but I really am desperate for a shower.'

'Of course I excuse you,' Shiona was quick to assure her. 'Take as long as you like. Dinner's not till eight.'

It was as the pair of them were passing through the doorway into the hall that Jake turned for a moment to catch Shiona's eye. He said not a word, but he didn't have to. The message in his eyes was loud and clear.

So, now that you've met her, you may go back to London just as soon as it's convenient.

Shiona dropped her gaze away. Yes, she was thinking, that's really all that's left for me to do.

'Can I go, too, and show Janice her room?' She glanced down suddenly to see Kirsty looking up at her.

She forced a smile. 'Of course you can, darling. Just make sure you don't get in her way.'

As the child bounded off, Shiona stood and watched the happy threesome cross the hallway and head for the stairs.

That was rich, she thought to herself wryly. I'm the one who's in the way!

CHAPTER FOUR

I'LL announce my departure over dinner, Shiona decided, as she slipped into a pretty blue dress in her room and combed back her mane of bright auburn hair. There was no point in her hanging around any longer. Kirsty, she was almost certain, would be in good hands with Janice.

Almost. . .

She frowned at her reflection in the mirror. Why did she say 'almost' and not 'entirely'? Almost, after all, wasn't nearly good enough. Kirsty's happiness was far too important to take a gamble with.

But then she thought again of that motherly, homely face that seemed to radiate a simple gentleness and warmth, and she felt sure that she was being over-cautious, perhaps even slightly prejudiced in her feelings about Janice. It wasn't an easy thing, after all, to approve of any fiancée of Jake's! Just by association, her sentiments tended towards the negative!

And you have no right to let such feelings affect your judgement, she rebuked herself sharply, slipping on her shoes. You have no right, out of prejudice, to stand in the way of Kirsty's chance to be a part of a proper family.

She sighed, and adjusted her pearl drop earrings

and the pretty gold locket at her throat. Help me to do the right thing, she prayed silently.

It was a quarter to eight when she stuck her head into the kitchen to have a quick word with Nettie before dinner.

'Is everything OK?' she enquired, smiling. 'Do you need a hand with anything?'

Pink-cheeked with her exertions, Nettie shook her head. 'Everything's fine, Miss Shiona,' she assured her, beaming happily, quite clearly in her element. 'Miss MacGregor is waiting in the drawing-room. As far as I know, Mr MacKay isn't down yet.'

Shiona nodded gratefully. 'I'll go and join her. Just give us a shout when you want us to move into the dining-room.'

Then, smiling to herself, she hurried along the corridor, rather looking forward to the opportunity to see Janice on her own.

But, as she reached the open door of the drawing-room and caught sight of Janice in the middle of the room, some instinct told her not to enter immediately. She took a step back into the shadows of the hallway and watched the other woman, her heart beating strangely. Playing the spy was not something that came naturally to her, but in this particular instance she sensed it was her duty.

Janice, needless to say, was quite unaware of her presence. Evidently, she believed herself to be quite unobserved.

She was circling the room with an almost predatory air, examining each painting, each piece of furniture, and it was not appreciation that was etched on her face. Her eyes were hard, her expression calculating. Pounds sterling, not aesthetics, were clearly on her mind.

Shiona felt a cold hand touch her heart. It was that same look she had caught a glimpse of earlier.

Then Shiona had preferred to deny the evidence of her eyes, but this time she could no longer do so. The woman was a gold-digger. In an instant she knew it. She felt her stomach squeeze sickly inside her.

'Good evening, Shiona. What are you waiting out here for?'

She spun round, startled, at the sound of Jake's voice, to find him standing at her elbow, blue eyes dark with condemnation as they looked down into her face.

'Don't you think you should be looking after our guest instead of prowling about out here in the corridor?'

'I was just going in.' She felt foolish and guilty, like a child caught with her fingers in the cake tin.

Jake pushed the door wider. 'Then what are you waiting for? I'm sure you've seen all there is to be seen.'

Shiona met his gaze then. 'Yes, I'm sure I have. I've certainly seen all I *need* to see.'

'There you are, the two of you!' They were interrupted at that moment as Janice came hurrying over to greet them. She kissed Jake's cheek and beamed at Shiona. 'I love your dress! That blue really suits you.'

'Thank you.' With an effort Shiona smiled back at

her. It was hard to believe that this generously smiling woman was the same predatory creature she'd been watching just a moment ago—but the image she had seen was seared in her brain, and suddenly she knew there was no way in the world that she could allow this woman to be a mother to Kirsty.

She turned away with mingled sadness and determination. 'I think we should go through to the dining-room now. Dinner must be nearly ready.'

Dinner itself was an uneasy experience. Like three actors in a play they each played their part, chatting inconsequentially about this and that, and pretending to be the best of friends. But, for her part, Shiona could barely wait for the iniquitous ordeal to come to an end. She desperately needed some time alone to think.

It was Janice who made the first move to end the evening. 'That was a fabulous meal,' she declared enthusiastically after the pudding plates had been cleared away. She stifled a yawn as she laid a hand on Jake's. 'But I suddenly feel totally exhausted. If you don't mind, darling, I think I'll skip coffee. All at once I feel a great need for bed.'

As Jake started to stand up, she shook her head and smiled. 'You stay where you are and finish dinner properly. Your bedtime isn't for hours yet!'

'Are you sure you'll be all right? You're feeling OK?' Suddenly he was frowning, his manner solicitous.

'I'm feeling fine. Just a little tired.' Janice patted his hand as she rose to her feet and turned to address

Shiona with one of her smiles. 'Goodnight, Shiona. I'll see you in the morning.'

Shiona nodded. 'Goodnight.' What an actress! she was thinking. From the look of her, butter wouldn't melt in her mouth!

A moment later, as the door closed behind Janice, Shiona toyed with the idea of making her own exit. But just then Nettie walked into the room, carrying a silver tray piled with coffee things.

'Only two for coffee?' she enquired with a slight frown. And as Jake nodded, Shiona reluctantly resigned herself to being trapped at the table with him for another little while. Nettie, after all, had gone to some trouble, with dishes of peppermint fondants and dark after-dinner chocolates, in addition to the steaming silver coffee-pot and the matching silver jug of thick fresh cream.

She laid the things out on the table, along with a decanter of brandy and some glasses, then took her leave as Jake told her, 'Thanks, Nettie. That'll be all. We can manage on our own.'

He picked up the silver coffee-pot as the door closed behind her, and poured the strong dark brew into the pretty Wedgwood cups. Then he reached for the brandy and tipped a measure into his own cup before offering to do the same with Shiona's.

But Shiona shook her head. 'No, thanks. I'll just have cream.'

'I like a nightcap after a busy day.' Jake took a mouthful of his coffee. 'I find it helps me to get a good night's sleep.'

Shiona glanced across at him, only half hearing

what he was saying. Has he any idea, she was wondering, that that woman is only marrying him for his money?

Then, as the blue eyes looked back at her with a flicker of curiosity, she responded automatically, 'So, you have trouble sleeping? I can't say that comes as any great surprise.'

He feigned incomprehension. 'Oh, and why would that be? Why would you suppose that I'm some kind of insomniac?'

Shiona shrugged, not needing to think about her answer. This sparring routine of theirs had grown so familiar that her brain had more or less switched to automatic.

'Something to do with the state of your conscience. I imagine you have a great deal to keep you awake at night.' As she spoke, her mind was still on Janice. How much would it hurt him, she was wondering, when he finally discovered the truth about his fiancée?

In the meantime, he was smiling. 'That's an interesting theory. I suppose you wouldn't care to elaborate further? I'd be most interested to know what you think keeps me awake.'

Shiona shrugged. 'Oh, I don't know the sordid details. And in a way I'm even a little surprised to hear that your conscience actually bothers you. I've always tended to think of you as rather lacking in conscience.'

'Like you, you mean?'

'No, not like me.'

'Is that why you sleep so soundly in your bed—

because you're conveniently incapable of suffering from guilt?'

'I have nothing to feel guilty about.'

'Yes, you would say that, wouldn't you?'

'And why would you deny that it's true?'

He did not answer her immediately, just continued to watch her across the table, his blue eyes suddenly as cold as ice. 'I think we both know the answer to that.'

'You mean Ryan, don't you?' She knew that look well. 'But I have nothing to feel guilty about, regarding Ryan.'

'So you've told me.'

'Then why won't you believe me?'

'Because the evidence speaks otherwise.' Jake's tone was bitter. That pain burned deep in his eyes again. 'You ruined my brother. My brother trusted you. And all you did was bleed him dry.'

Shiona's stomach clenched like a fist within her. That accusation was like a blow to the midriff, still as hurtful as ever, no matter how often she heard it. She was filled with an overwhelming desire to strike back at him, and suddenly she knew exactly how she could do it.

Are you aware that Janice doesn't really love you? Are you aware she's only marrying you for your money?

The words swarmed through her mind as she glared furiously back at him, but somehow she couldn't bring herself to say them. Instead, she said, 'I've decided to fight you. Over custody of Kirsty. I won't let you take her.'

There was a momentary pause at this sudden switch in the conversation. Jake drained his coffee-cup and laid it down on the saucer. 'Is this decision of yours just to try and thwart me, or do you have any particular reason?'

'I have a very good reason, as it happens.' She held his eyes. 'I don't like Janice. I don't believe she'd make a good mother for Kirsty.'

To her surprise, he laughed. 'You're so damned predictable. You just don't give up when there's a profit to be made.'

Again Shiona was filled with the urge to say it, to hurt him as he had so often hurt her. But he wouldn't believe it even if she said it, she decided. He'd simply accuse her of being spiteful.

He was still watching her across the table. 'So why don't you like Janice? Tell me. I'm interested.'

'Interested in my opinion? I sincerely doubt it.' Shiona sat back in her seat and narrowed her eyes at him. 'I just don't like her. I don't intend to elaborate.'

'Female intuition?' He was mocking.

'Something like that.'

'Is that why you were spying on her when I caught you out in the hallway? Were you hoping to catch her stealing the silver?'

He was closer than he thought, Shiona thought with a small shiver. She laid down her napkin. Suddenly she felt tired, and she had no desire to get into a harangue with him. 'If you don't mind, I think I'll go to bed.'

'I'll tell you something before you go. . .' Jake's eyes were on her, biting into her. 'In spite of your intuition, my dear Shiona, Janice is a much nicer person than you, and far more suited to be Kirsty's mother.'

He paused for an instant. 'And if you really are serious about pursuing your ridiculous claim for custody, I shall make damned sure that the court knows all about you. As beautiful and as wholesome as you may be on the outside, I shall reveal you for the black-hearted trickster that you are. The woman who exploited and ruined my brother will never be appointed guardian to my sister!'

Suddenly Shiona was trembling with anger. 'How dare you threaten me?' she spat out across the table at him. 'How dare you threaten to go to court and lie about me?'

She jumped to her feet, her stomach churning with emotion, and jarred one hip violently against the edge of the table, sending her untouched coffee-cup toppling sideways on its saucer.

'I won't have to lie. I shall simply tell the truth. That will be more than enough to put an end to your claims.'

It was that superior, malicious arrogance of his that triggered Shiona's reaction. As she reached for the coffee-cup, half of its contents now in the saucer, all she intended to do was right it. But as her trembling fingers closed around it, a more satisfying notion flew into her head.

'You wouldn't recognise the truth if you found it in your brandy glass!' Furiously, she hurled the accusation at him. Then, in the very same breath, she snatched up the toppled coffee-cup and flung the lukewarm contents in his face.

Then she was turning on her heel and heading for the door, anxious to make a speedy escape.

But as she reached the door, one hand on the door-handle, suddenly an iron band clamped round her arm. She was swung round forcefully, so that her breath gasped from her body, then with equal force she was flung against the door.

'And what was that meant to prove?' Steel fingers gripped her arm, while the fingers of his other hand closed tightly around her chin. He thrust a face dark with anger into hers. 'Was that meant to convince me what a sweet innocent you are?'

To her dismay Shiona saw that her aim had been off. The coffee had simply splattered across the front of his shirt. 'I wish I'd thrown the coffee-pot!' she seethed at him defiantly. 'I wish it had been boiling and I'd poured it over your damned head!'

'Yes, I'll bet you do.' He gave her a shake, forcing her chin up as he glared down into her face. 'A young woman with a nasty, vicious nature like yours is capable of wishing all sorts of evil things.'

'It would be no more than you deserve! And one day I'll do it! One day I'll get back at you, Jake MacKay!'

'Get back at me for what? For seeing right through you? For being the only male in my family to recognise you for what you are?'

'You really believe that, don't you? You think you're so clever! You're so damned self-righteous you make me sick!'

'So put me right, my dear, since you keep insisting I'm mistaken. Finally reveal the sweet-scented truth about yourself that has been so cruelly denied for all these years.' He smiled sarcastically. 'Believe me, I'm all ears!'

She was standing pinned against the door, her hands flattened against it, her escape entirely blocked by Jake's powerful form. As he spoke, he had deliberately moved even closer. She dared not flex a muscle or she would be pressed hard against him.

'I wouldn't waste my breath!' Her hazel eyes flayed him. 'So just kindly let me go, and stop playing the heavy.'

His fingers caressed her jaw. 'Don't be in such a hurry. I'm giving you a chance to convince me. Take it!'

'I don't want your chances! I don't want anything from you! Just do me a favour and let me go!' Suddenly she was almost suffocating from the oppressive agony of his nearness.

'You have nothing to say, do you? Just lies and more lies.' He took his hand from her arm and slid his fingers through her hair. 'And how well those temptress lips of yours know how to lie.' His eyes dropped to her mouth, causing her stomach to flip over. With that sensuous, slow gaze of his it was as though he had kissed her.

Shiona held her breath. 'Please let me go. Look, I'm sorry I threw the coffee at you.' Anything to make him release her!

His eyes slid back to hers. 'More lies,' he murmured. And as his hand caressed her scalp, his expression had subtly altered. 'I bet you tell some whoppers to all your lovers. I bet the poor devils don't know whether they're coming or going!'

He was driving her crazy the way he was holding her and the way he was looking down at her with smouldering blue eyes. She turned her face away. 'Let me go!' she croaked desperately. 'All I ask of you is that you please let me go.'

'Why, my dear Shiona? Am I hurting you?' There was amusement in Jake's voice, but there was something else as well.

'Yes,' she lied. 'And, what's more, you're suffocating me.' She took an elaborate deep breath. 'I can scarcely breathe.'

She felt him smile, but she did not look at him. And it was true, she was finding breathing increasingly difficult, thanks to the wild commotion in her heart.

Just as they had that other time when he had briefly held her, her senses were reacting with a will of their own. With her mind and her intellect Shiona knew that she hated him, yet, shamelessly, wantonly, her body still craved him. She could have wept for the agony of raw longing that burned through her.

She had never been kissed by him in all the years she had known him—apart from a brotherly peck on the cheek. But she had dreamed of it endlessly in those days when she had adored him. Her imagination had run wild as she had fantasised tirelessly about how it would feel to have him hold her, his mouth pressed in passion against her own.

Now suddenly she could feel the pleasure such imaginings had aroused uncurling in a warm spiral in the pit of her stomach. All at once a bright fire seemed to burn through her veins, making her skin glow and causing her limbs to tremble.

She shuddered helplessly and closed her eyes. 'Jake. . . Oh, Jake. . .' Her voice trailed off. She no longer had any idea what it was she wanted to say to him.

'Yes, my sweet temptress?' His warm breath fanned her face. She felt him move closer, his fingers tangling in her hair. 'I'm listening, my sweet temptress. Tell me what you want?'

I want nothing! Let me go! But she did not speak the words, only whispered them despairingly inside her head. She felt like that fish caught by the curlew, one part of her praying that he would spit her out again, the other, perversely, longing for him to swallow her up.

And then, to her astonishment, she heard herself say, 'Shouldn't you go upstairs and see how Janice is? I'm sure she's waiting for you to look in and say goodnight.'

'You think so, do you?' There was a harsh note in his voice.

'I also think you'd be better employed looking after your fiancée instead of bullying me.'

'Is that what I've been doing?'

'What else would you call it?' At last she dared to meet his eyes again. 'And you ought to know by now that it's a waste of time.'

There was a dark look in his eyes as he continued

to look down at her, but as she proceeded to wriggle away from him he made no move to stop her. 'You're right. Everything with you is a waste of time.' He smiled a harsh smile and stepped away from the door. 'Go on. Get out of my sight before I lose patience with you totally.'

Without a word, Shiona hastened to oblige, turning on her heel and snatching hold of the door-handle, then, with a final crushing glance at him, stepping out into the hall.

But as she hurried up the stairs to the sanctuary of her bedroom, what filled her mind was the stark, appalling thought of the treachery she had so nearly perpetrated on herself.

If, back there in the dining-room, he had tried to kiss her, she knew she would have made no effort to stop him. And worse. Even now the thought of that kiss, that for one moment had hovered so dangerously between them, writhed inside her like a bitter, cruel torment.

For she had longed for it desperately. And, to her shame, she did still.

It was the longest weekend Shiona had ever endured. A hundred miserable lifetimes condensed into two wretched days.

What made it even worse was that she had to pretend to enjoy it. For Kirsty's sake she had to put on a bright face.

Jake had organised a mass of entertainments— including a visit to Stirling Castle, a leisurely hill-walk over the Braes of Balquhidder, and a trip to the legendary Rob Roy's grave. And, although they were all enjoyable excursions, to Shiona they felt like a dose of purgatory. For they meant that she was forced to spend the entire weekend in Jake's company.

Of course, she had an option. She could have declined to accompany them. But even if Kirsty hadn't insisted, she would have taken part anyway. In spite of everything, being with Kirsty was fun, and, besides, she wanted to keep an eye on Janice, and perhaps gather more proof regarding her own 'intuition'.

This she did to her quiet satisfaction, thanks to a careless slip by Janice. After their walk across the Braes of Balquhidder, Shiona and Janice got back to the car first. Janice climbed into the leather-scented Mercedes and looked around her with a self-satisfied smile.

'Quite a car,' she murmured half to herself. 'I shall quite enjoy getting used to this lifestyle.'

'I'm sure you will.' Shiona spoke quietly. 'And, after all, if you haven't got it yourself, it's a pretty smart move to marry into money.'

'My philosophy precisely.' Janice had said it without thinking, but then an instant later she realised her lapse. 'Just my little joke.' She forced a sweet smile. 'I would never dream of marrying for anything less than love.'

'Of course you wouldn't.' Poor Jake, Shiona thought, the sentiment surprising her a little. Surely Jake deserved a wife precisely like Janice—the gold-digger he'd always accused Shiona of being.

But that was not what concerned her. What concerned her was Kirsty. And now she was doubly
determined that Janice would never be her mother.

It was a relief when the weekend was finally over.
On Sunday night Shiona got ready for bed, knowing
that by next morning Janice would be gone. At least
in the meantime there would be no more cosy three-
somes to endure, and she could put her mind to
deciding how to conduct her battle to save Kirsty.

But even more of a reprieve was lurking round the
corner. As she was brushing her teeth, the phone in
the hall began to ring—and was answered almost
immediately, she guessed, by Jake. Then, a few
minutes later, as she climbed beneath the bedovers,
propping herself against the pillows to read a chapter
of her book, she heard footsteps coming up the stairs.
Jake, she thought idly, on his way to bed.

But, to her astonishment, a moment later there
came a knock on her door. She pulled the covers up
around her. 'Who is it?' she called, sensing that she
knew.

'It's me. I have to talk to you. Can I come in?'

She pulled the covers higher. 'Of course. If you
must.'

Jake smiled as he saw her. 'Quite the little virgin.
You'd think no man had ever seen you in your
nightgown before.'

No man ever had, she could truthfully have
answered him. But she simply snapped instead,
'What do you want?'

As he stepped into the room, the door swung shut
behind him, causing a skitter of claustrophobia to

make Shiona catch her breath. Please open the door, she felt like telling him. But she knew he would only mock her, so with an effort she refrained.

'That was one of my senior managers on the phone.' Though still dressed, he had removed his jacket and tie, and the top few buttons of his shirt were undone. 'There's been a bit of a crisis over the weekend—some vital supplies have been held up— and, apparently, my presence is urgently required.'

Shiona raised her eyebrows. They're more than welcome to you, she was thinking. 'How unfortunate,' she observed with an insincere smile.

'Yes, I figured you'd probably be pretty broken up.' Jake stuffed his hands into the pockets of his trousers. 'This means I'll have to leave tomorrow morning with Janice. I hope to be back before the end of the week.'

'That serious?' She smiled again. 'Well, I won't try to stop you. And please feel free to stay away as long as you please.'

Jake laughed softly and shook his head at her. 'You're so damned predictable. I can always tell exactly what you're going to say next.'

'Then that makes two of us,' Shiona countered, meeting the blue eyes that suddenly seemed to have grown darker beneath the sweep of thick black lashes. 'I can always tell what's in *your* mind. All I have to do is think of the most unpleasant thing possible.'

'So, what's in my mind now?' He had taken a step towards her. Suddenly he seemed to be standing very close to the bed. He paused and looked down at her, a strange smile hovering on his lips. 'Go on, tell me, since you know me so well.'

Shiona shivered beneath the bedclothes, though her flesh was suddenly burning. And somehow she couldn't stop her gaze from straying to the triangle of naked chest where his shirt buttons were open. She longed to reach out and press her open palm against it.

She tried to cast the thought from her, but it stayed stubbornly with her as he took another small step towards her.

'Aren't you going to tell me?' He was smiling strangely. 'It's not like you to be so backward.' Then, to her horror, he reached out and touched her hair. 'How utterly tempting you look lying there.'

Shiona caught her breath. Her heart was suddenly pounding. She felt a twist of raw burning longing in her loins. 'When will you be leaving?' she enquired crassly, not quite daring to meet his eyes.

'Long before you're up, my sweet Shiona. Unless, of course, you particularly want to see me off. I can easily wake you, if you wish.'

'Please don't bother yourself.' She forced herself to speak calmly. 'It's quite enough for me just to know that you're going.'

'You'll be good while I'm gone?' His fingers touched her hair again, stroking the bright strands that fell against the pillow. 'You won't do anything I wouldn't approve of?'

'Like what, for example?' Her voice was husky. She longed to turn her cheek and press it against his palm.

'I mean you'll look after Kirsty?'

'Of course I'll look after Kirsty.'

'You won't go gallivanting about, looking for excitement, and forget where your first responsibility lies?'

Shiona managed a small laugh. 'I think I'd have a hard job trying to find the sort of excitement you're referring to here, around Loch Lomond.'

'Yes, I think you probably would.' Jake smiled in agreement. 'It's not the liveliest place in the world.'

That's why I like it. Shiona almost said it. Suddenly she desperately wanted him to know the truth. The sort of 'gallivanting about' that he seemed always to associate with her had never been a part of her life at all.

She looked into his face. But he would never believe her. And she already knew how much it hurt to keep trying and trying, only to fail.

'Goodnight, Shiona.'

As she continued to gaze up at him, a million thoughts writhing around in her head, all at once he bent towards her, making her heart stop, and planted a soft kiss on her cheek.

Then, almost in the same breath, he turned on his heel and strode out of the room without another word.

CHAPTER FIVE

IT APPEARED to be a week for crises.

On the Wednesday after Jake returned to Edinburgh to deal with the crisis at MacKay Contracting, Shiona received a frantic phone call from Desmond, her second-in-command in London.

'You've got to come down,' he urged her, close to panic. 'That big fashion gala we've got scheduled for Paris is going to fall through unless you have a word with the organisers. I've done my damnedest, but they insist on speaking to you.'

'Oh, lord!' Shiona wailed. 'Can't it wait till next week? There's no way I can manage to come down at the moment.' With perfect bad timing Inge, the au pair, had left that very morning on a few days' holiday, and tomorrow was Nettie the housekeeper's day off. Who would look after Kirsty if Shiona was to go dashing down to London?

'It's up to you, darling, but next week will be too late. If you want the Paris gala to go ahead, you'd be wise to get down here before the weekend.'

Shiona felt like weeping. She couldn't jeopardise the gala. She had been planning it for months now, and it was vitally important. Already her knitwear had gained a small foothold on the Continent. This gala could finally secure her position.

'OK, I'll do my best,' she promised Desmond. 'If

there's any way to fix it, I'll be there before the weekend.'

As she put down the phone, her brain was working overtime. How on earth could she possibly manage it? Then, in a flash, the perfect solution occurred to her. Instantly she rushed out into the garden to find Kirsty.

The little girl, newly returned from school, was playing with a ball beside the sundial. Shiona took her hands in hers and knelt down beside her. 'How would you like to go with Aunt Shiona down to London?'

The child's eyes widened. 'On the train? I've never been on a train before.'

'On the train, if you like,' Shiona nodded, quickly amending her original plan to fly. If they caught the Sleeper tonight instead of flying down tomorrow morning, it would work out equally convenient. 'Just for one day,' she told the bright-eyed Kirsty. 'We'll come back again tomorrow night.'

'On the train again?'

'On the train again.' Shiona gathered her up in her arms and kissed her. Then she held her at arm's length and frowned a little. 'But you must promise me not to tell Uncle Jake. You must promise me that this will be our little secret.'

'I promise.' Kirsty nodded. 'But what about Miss Brewster? We'll have to tell Miss Brewster that I won't be at school.'

'Don't you worry about Miss Brewster. Aunt Shiona will phone her and explain everything,' she promised. Thank heavens, she was thinking, that she was on good terms with Kirsty's teacher. Speaking to Miss Brewster wouldn't be a problem.

The next thing Shiona did was phone Glasgow Central Station and book two sleepers on the overnight train that left just before midnight. They would arrive in London just after six, giving her an entire day to sort out her problems.

As she quickly packed a bag before preparing dinner, it suddenly struck her what a risk she was taking. If Jake found out he would have her guts for garters!

She pursed her lips determinedly. But he wouldn't find out. How on earth could he? she reassured herself.

A couple of hours later she was bundling a sleepy but highly excited Kirsty into the back seat of the car, then heading towards Glasgow with a huge sigh of relief. Her worst fear had been that Jake would show up before they had even left Lomond View.

That was one hurdle passed, she thought, gripping the steering-wheel. But, all the same, she wouldn't feel safe until they were finally aboard the train and it was heading south out of Central Station. Only then could she really afford to relax.

Kirsty chattered excitedly throughout the journey, helping to keep Shiona's mind off her anxieties. By the time they'd parked the car and were hurrying towards the station platform, the little girl's enthusiasm had soothed her tattered nerves, and she was really looking forward to their day together in London.

Once inside the tiny sleeping compartment, Kirsty

changed quickly into her pyjamas. 'Can I have the top bunk, Aunt Shiona?' she wheedled.

Shiona rumpled her hair. 'If you promise not to fall out.'

'I won't fall out. I'm not a baby!' As the little girl clambered up, as agile as a monkey, Shiona started to pull her own pyjamas from the bag. But a moment later her heart stopped in her chest as a sharp tap sounded on the door.

Surely it couldn't be Jake? she thought in startled panic. Surely it wasn't possible that he had tracked them down?

She held her breath and opened the door a crack—then almost fainted with relief as the steward enquired politely, 'Will you be requiring tea or coffee in the morning?'

'Coffee, please,' she grinned, so relieved she could have hugged him.

He smiled in return. 'Sleep well,' he told her.

Shiona closed the door just as the train began to move, leaving Glasgow and the threat of Jake behind them. She turned to smile at Kirsty. 'We're on our way. When you wake up we'll be in London.'

Kirsty smiled at her drowsily. 'I like the train. I'd like to sleep on the train every night.'

Minutes later, feeling suddenly totally exhausted by all the nervous tension of the past few hours, Shiona kissed the already sleeping Kirsty goodnight, then climbed into her own bunk and closed her eyes.

I've done it! she thought with a sweet sense of triumph. For once, I've actually outwitted Jake!

Her only faint regret was that Jake would never know!

It seemed like only moments after Shiona had fallen asleep that the light snapped on in the compartment and a strong hand was dragging her from her bunk.

'Get dressed!' a voice snarled. 'In double-quick time!' The hand shook her violently. 'You deceitful little brat!'

Shiona blinked her eyes open, half wondering if this was a nightmare, her gaze flickering automatically to the upper bunk where Kirsty was still lying peacefully asleep. Then, still a little dopey, she glanced back with a frown at the dark, menacing figure standing over her.

'Jake?' she frowned. 'What are you doing here?'

'Don't waste time asking questions! Just get dressed!' he repeated. 'You and Kirsty are leaving the train!'

Shiona rubbed her eyes. 'Are we in London already?' She glanced quickly at her watch. 'We can't be. It's only half-past one.'

'I already told you not to waste time asking questions! I want the pair of you dressed and off this train in five minutes—or I swear I'll drag you off in your pyjamas!'

He snatched the trousers and sweater that hung from a hanger on the wall, and threw them at her, the gesture violent. 'I'm not joking, Shiona. You're in serious trouble. This time you've really gone too far!'

So saying he backed out into the corridor again,

where Shiona caught a glimpse of the frowning faces
of a couple of uniformed railway officials. And suddenly she was wide awake. It looked as though she
really was in serious trouble.

It took her less than a minute to pull on her clothes
and a couple more to dress the still sleeping Kirsty.
She gathered the little girl into her arms, grabbed her
bag and headed for the door. Suddenly her stomach
was churning with anxiety.

Gently but firmly, careful not to wake the child,
Jake took Kirsty from her as she stepped out into the
corridor. Then, with a nod in the direction of the
railwaymen—'Thanks for your assistance, and for
holding up the train'—he had grabbed Shiona uncer-
emoniously by the wrist and was dragging her
towards the door.

She half stumbled behind him, her anxiety growing. What was going on? Why had they held up the
train?

From the signs on the station platform she could
see now where they were. And they were nowhere
near London. They were in Carlisle, just a few miles
south of the Scottish-English border. She shivered in
the hostile, cold night air. What was this melodram-
atic gesture of Jake's all about?

With Kirsty still sleeping soundly against his
shoulder, Jake strode towards the exit of the deserted
station and out to where his car was parked.

So he had driven down from Edinburgh to inter-
cept the train. He must indeed have been utterly
determined to thwart her—not to say very certain

that she was on the train. Shiona wondered irritably
how he had found out.

As he pulled open the passenger door for her, she
scowled at him defiantly. 'Where are you taking us?'
she demanded to know.

'Perhaps where I'm taking you is to the nearest
police station. . .' His tone was harsh, his eyes like
thunder. 'To turn you in for abducting a minor.'

Shiona's eyes shot wide open. 'To *what*?' she
protested.

'You heard,' he cut back at her. 'As you're well
aware, Kirsty happens to be in my interim custody.
She may not be taken out of Scotland without special
permission.'

Just for a moment the blood left Shiona's face. For
some idiotic reason it had never crossed her mind
that she might be doing something illegal. The only
thing she'd been worried about was Jake finding out.

But, all the same, he was over-reacting. She turned
to glare at him and made an effort to resist as he
made to propel her into the passenger seat. 'You
know perfectly well I wasn't trying to abduct her! I
had to go to London and I couldn't leave her. And
anyway, I was planning to bring her back tomorrow.'

But he was clearly in no mood for listening to her
excuses. 'Just get in before I throw you in!' he
commanded brusquely. 'I'm not interested in hearing
what you were planning to do.'

No, she hadn't thought he would be! Shiona threw
him a harsh look as, shrugging off his hand, she
climbed into the passenger seat. When had he ever
been interested in hearing her side of things?

He slammed the door shut, then with infinite care proceeded to lay Kirsty on the back seat. A moment later he was climbing into the driver's seat. 'What an irredeemably selfish person you are to do something like this to an innocent little girl.'

'Kirsty was enjoying herself!' Shiona instantly defended. 'I would never have taken her if I'd thought it would upset her.'

In response Jake gave an angry little laugh. 'Save it for the police. They might listen to your excuses.'

'Yes, I think they might.' Shiona was defiant. 'In fact I'm sure they'll be much more reasonable than you. At least they'll *listen* to what I have to say!' She sat back in her seat and kept her eyes fixed ahead of her. 'So by all means take me, and let's sort this whole thing out.'

If he thought he could scare her with his stupid little threats, he would soon find out that he was mistaken!

But, fifteen minutes later, it wasn't the police station, but one of the local hotels that they drew up in front of.

'Take your bag and get out,' Jake told her without looking at her. Then, as she obeyed, he was reaching into the back seat of the car and lifting out Kirsty, who had never once stirred.

'I thought you were taking me to the police station.' Shiona eyed him challengingly over the bonnet of the car. 'Don't tell me you've had a sudden change of heart?'

'Perhaps I've decided it can wait until tomorrow.'

His tone was as icy as a glacier. 'I think our first priority should be to get Kirsty to bed.'

Shiona couldn't have agreed more, but her tone was taunting as she told him, 'What a pity you'll have to wait until tomorrow to see me led away in chains.'

'For such a pleasing spectacle I don't mind waiting. It'll give me something to look forward to.' With a brief, mocking smile, he turned away and hurried up the steps to the hotel lobby, his back as hostile as a roll of barbed wire.

Once inside, he turned and handed her Kirsty. 'Perhaps you can look after her for five minutes while I go and book the rooms?' His gaze grazed hers. 'You'll manage that, will you?'

Shiona sliced him a look as she took the child to her bosom. 'I always look after her!' she snapped back.

A couple of minutes later he was snapping his fingers at her, inviting her to follow him to the lift. He took Kirsty again, and handed Shiona a key. 'Second floor. Room 207.'

The room was warm and comfortable, with a big double bed and its own adjoining little bathroom.

Jake laid Kirsty on the bed. 'You'd better get her into her pyjamas,' he told Shiona. Then he turned— so Shiona thought—to go off to his own room. But instead he headed for the bathroom. 'I'm going to have a very quick shower.'

What was he up to? Shiona frowned. 'Wouldn't you be better to have it in your own room?'

He turned then to look at her, his expression faintly mocking. 'This *is* my own room, my dear Shiona.'

'Then where is mine?'

'Yours is right here.'

'You mean to tell me we're sharing a room?'

He nodded. 'That's right. You've got it in one.'

Shiona took a deep breath. 'But that's out of the question. I have no intention of sharing a room with you.'

'Then you must sleep out in the corridor.' The blue eyes were shuttered. 'This is the only room they have.'

'And where are we all supposed to sleep? The three of us all together in one bed?' She shuddered pointedly. 'That may appeal to you, but there's no way I would consider it even for a moment.'

'I quite agree.' He was watching her closely, and she could not quite make out the expression in his eyes. 'Three in a bed would be something of a crush. However. . .' He paused. 'If you look over in the corner, there's a little ante-room with a single bed—intended, so I believe, to accommodate a child.'

Shiona followed his gaze and saw the ante-room door that had quite escaped her notice before. Then once more she snapped her eyes back to Jake. 'That's still not good enough,' she protested. 'I have no intention of sharing a bed with you!'

He smiled an amused smile. 'You needn't worry. I'm so damned tired after the drive down here that I doubt I'll have the energy for anything more than sleep.'

In spite of herself, at the way he looked at her,

Shiona felt a flutter in the pit of her stomach. Even in this far from congenial situation the thought of sharing a bed with Jake made her pulse beat faster and warmth rise to her cheeks.

Yet in the very same instant the warm flutter died away to be replaced by the weight of cold reality. How could she, even fleetingly, entertain such a thought for a man who despised her so deeply and so openly?

She glared across at him. 'I'd rather sleep on the floor than have to share a bed with you.'

The blue eyes narrowed as he regarded her for a moment. 'Don't worry, dear Shiona. For once, I share your view. I can think of nothing less appealing than climbing into bed with you—which is why I intend to sleep in the ante-room. You and Kirsty can share the bed in here.'

He turned away sharply. 'Now, if you don't mind, I'm going to have that shower and get my head down. I'd like to get a little sleep tonight.'

As the door of the bathroom closed behind him, Shiona picked up her travel bag with a flash of irritation. So, he had been winding her up about their sharing the same bed, amusing himself at her expense! She pulled out her own and Kirsty's pyjamas. Well, let him have his little joke! All that really mattered, after all, was that there would be a stout door to separate the two of them tonight!

It was just at that moment that Kirsty stirred. She blinked at Shiona and half sat up on the bed. 'Are we in London?' she wanted to know.

Shiona hugged her. 'No, we're not in London.

We're somewhere much nicer. We're in Carlisle.' She kissed the child warmly. 'And, what's more,' she told her, 'there's an extra-special surprise for you waiting behind that door. . .'

As she nodded towards the bathroom, right on cue it opened, and Jake, dressed in trousers with a towel slung round his neck, came walking with a broad smile into the room.

Kirsty grinned from ear to ear. 'Uncle Jake!' she squealed happily. Then she frowned a little. 'Why aren't we on the train?'

Jake perched on the edge of the bed beside her. 'I'm afraid that's my fault,' he confessed. 'I got Aunt Shiona to leave the train early so we could all spend the night together here.'

Shiona nodded in agreement. 'I hope you don't mind? We'll go on the train to London some other time.'

'OK.' The child nodded, apparently content with that promise. Then she rubbed her eyes. 'I'm sleepy,' she sighed.

Five minutes later she was tucked up in bed, sleeping happily once again, while Jake had retreated to his little ante-room. Shiona gathered up her pyjamas and headed for the bathroom, her mind retracing the events of the night.

Now that she had calmed down it was very clear to her that her actions had been rash, to say the least. She had broken the law unwittingly, but still she had broken it, and if Jake was really determined he could make her pay for it.

If he decided to report her, he could then use her

lapse against her when the custody case finally came
to court. It would not be too difficult for his legal
representative to brand her as rash and irrespon-
sible—scarcely attributes the judge would be looking
for in little Kirsty's potential guardian!

She washed quickly and undressed. Somehow she
must convince Jake that it would be wrong to judge
her harshly. She may have acted impetuously, but
she'd intended no malice, and she'd always had
Kirsty's best interests at heart.

And now would be a good time to talk to him, she
decided, as she pulled on her pyjamas and brushed
back her hair. His mood had softened after his little
chat with Kirsty. And besides, she knew that if she
waited till morning she would simply toss and turn
all night.

As she stepped out of the bathroom she stole a
quick glance at the bed, just to check that Kirsty was
still sleeping. Then, taking a deep breath, she crossed
to the little ante-room and tapped with her knuckles
on the door.

'Jake, are you awake? I'd like to speak to you.'

There was no reply, just an impatient grunt that at
least confirmed that he wasn't sleeping. Shiona
pushed the door open and stepped inside, pulling it
to again before she tiptoed towards the bed.

'I'm sorry to bother you,' she whispered. 'But I
have to talk to you. I promise you it'll only take a
minute.'

The only light was the crack of light down the side
of the door. She could just make him out as he rolled

over to face her. 'What the hell do you want? Can't you let a man sleep?'

'I'm sorry, Jake.' She squatted beside him, as he propped himself up on one elbow to scowl back at her. 'I can't sleep without telling you what really happened.'

He expelled his breath impatiently. 'What are you talking about? I already know exactly what happened.'

'No, you don't.' Shiona hurried on quickly. 'You seem to think I was planning to abduct Kirsty. I wasn't. I was merely taking her down to London for a day. I was planning to bring her back on the Sleeper tonight.'

'I'll bet you were.' He regarded her sceptically. 'And what made you think that poor little Kirsty was so desperately in need of a day-trip to London?'

Shiona shook her head. 'It wasn't a day-trip. I *had* to go to London. There's a crisis on at the studio. And, since Inge's on holiday and it's Nettie's day off, there was no way I could leave her at Lomond View.' She peered at him through the semi-darkness. 'That's the only reason I took her.'

Jake seemed unmoved by her explanation. 'So why couldn't this tale of yours have kept until morning?' In the half-light of the room his eyes were scornful, the set of his jaw mocking and hard. 'Do you perhaps believe a man is more susceptible to persuasion when he's lying in bed naked in the middle of the night?'

Shiona blinked, taken aback by his accusation. 'Of course not!' she protested. 'The thought never occurred to me!' Yet, though it was perfectly true, she backed away a little, for suddenly she was quite overpoweringly conscious of his virile naked form beneath the blankets.

He simply smiled, openly disbelieving, and raised himself a little higher on his elbow. His eyes seemed to darken as his gaze roved over her. 'Perhaps you also believe that a man is more easily persuaded by a beautiful, semi-naked girl.'

'I'm not semi-naked!' All at once Shiona's heart was pounding. The broad, sinewy shoulders and the powerfully muscled chest suddenly seemed to fill her vision. She swallowed drily, backing away another centimetre. 'I'm wearing a perfectly respectable pair of pyjamas!'

'Not from where I'm lying, you're not.'

As his eyes drifted pointedly downwards to her bosom, Shiona saw his free hand reach out towards her. She started to spring away—'What the devil do you think you're doing?'—and simultaneously glanced down at her pyjama-jacket. And to her horror she could see that in her haste to come and speak to him she had only buttoned the bottom two buttons, and the way she was sitting, crouching forward slightly, one smooth, firm breast was entirely exposed.

Colour flooded her face as she tried to struggle to her feet, desperate to evade the hand that was stretched towards her. But he was far too quick for her. As she staggered awkwardly, he grabbed firm hold of the sagging pyjama-jacket, arresting her flight as he held her there.

Her skin was burning as she thought he might

touch her. Any minute she expected to feel his hand on her breast.

But instead he pulled the jacket closed, the gesture deliberately rough and contemptuous. 'Cover yourself, Shiona,' he admonished her harshly. 'I'm not remotely interested in your crude efforts at seduction. You may have succeeded with my brother, but I've warned you before you're wasting your time with me!'

As he released her she stumbled to her feet, her face on fire, her heart thumping within her. 'Don't flatter yourself! I wasn't trying to seduce you!' She felt angry and hurt and deeply humiliated.

He regarded her coldly. 'I've told you, I'm not Ryan. You won't find it quite so easy to manipulate me.' Then, with a look that froze her, he turned away. 'Go now!' he commanded. 'Leave me in peace!'

Shiona bit her lip. Suddenly she felt like weeping. Then without another word she rose to her feet, hating the huddled figure lying with his back to her.

'My pleasure!' she muttered defiantly to herself, as she hurried from the ante-room, closed the door behind her, and headed for the sanctuary of her own bed.

'It's time to get up!' Kirsty was shaking her. 'Uncle Jake says we've to be down for breakfast in a quarter of an hour.'

Shiona struggled to consciousness and rubbed her eyes. 'What time is it?' she mumbled hoarsely. She felt as though she'd been asleep for about five minutes!

'It's eight o'clock. Uncle Jake says it's late. He says we've got to be on the road by nine o'clock at the latest.'

With a huge yawn Shiona pulled herself upright. Then she reached out and hugged little Kirsty tightly. 'How are you feeling? Did you sleep all right?'

Kirsty nodded. 'Yes, and I'm hungry. Can I have toast and honey for breakfast?'

'Of course you can. You can have anything you like.' Shiona swung her legs down on to the carpet. 'I'll race you. Let's see who's dressed and ready first!'

Just under twenty minutes later, with Kirsty having won the contest easily, the two of them were heading downstairs to the breakfast-room. And, as they walked through the doorway of the big, sunny room, the dark-haired man at the table by the window glanced up from his copy of *The Times*.

He looked immaculate and well rested, as though he had slept for twelve hours instead of a scanty, meagre five. She had circles like bicycle tyres under her eyes, but there was no sign of even the faintest shadow beneath his!

Damn him! Shiona thought. How does he do it?

As Kirsty scampered towards him, Jake laid down his newspaper, kissed her on the cheek, then glanced up at Shiona. 'So you made it, after all.' His tone was lightly sarcastic. 'You looked as though you were set to sleep all day.'

She probably would have done if she had been left to her own devices! But she feigned disdain as she sat down opposite him. 'I have far too busy a day planned for anything so self-indulgent.'

Before he could comment a waitress arrived to take her and Kirsty's order for bacon and eggs and toast and honey. But once the woman had gone, Jake raised one dark eyebrow. 'Perhaps you wouldn't mind enlightening me as to what you're planning?'

Shiona paused before answering to pour some orange juice for Kirsty. Then, her eyes on his face, she poured some for herself. 'Of course, it all rather depends,' she put to him in a wry tone, 'on the outcome of our visit to the police station. If they decide to arrest me and throw me in gaol, my plans will have to be drastically altered. . .'

She saw a flicker of something cross his eyes. Possibly amusement. Possibly something else. He topped up his coffee-cup before answering, 'And what do you plan to do if they don't?'

Shiona shrugged. 'Catch the first flight to London. As I told you, there's a crisis on at the studio. They need me there to sort it out.'

He took a mouthful of his coffee. 'So that story you told me. . . You mean to say it was true, after all?'

'Of course it was true. Why would I lie to you?'

That struck him as funny. He gave a small laugh. 'To save your hide, that's why you'd lie to me. And also because you're in the habit of doing so.'

Shiona sighed impatiently. 'Surely even you couldn't have seriously thought that I intended abducting Kirsty?' She cast a quick, cautious glance at the little girl, fearing that she might have over-heard, but Kirsty had slid down from her chair and was quite clearly totally absorbed in watching the antics of the hotel cat through the window. 'I would never subject Kirsty to that sort of tug-of-love.'

He regarded her for a moment as though considering what she'd told him. 'OK,' he said at last, 'I shan't turn you in. I've decided to let you off this time.'

As she smiled smugly—she'd suspected he wouldn't—he deliberately threw her a frosty glance.

'But don't ever try a trick like that again,' he warned. 'There was no excuse for it, whatever the circumstances. All you had to do was telephone me, and I would have come at once to look after Kirsty.'

'I didn't think of that.' It was true, she hadn't. 'I took her because there was no one else around to look after her.' She tilted her chin at him. 'No harm would have come to her. She would have enjoyed her little trip to London.'

'Perhaps she would.' Jake smiled enigmatically. 'But the law is the law. It's not there to be broken. So don't do it again.' He held her eyes a moment. 'Next time I really will turn you in.'

Shiona took a mouthful of her orange juice. 'I'm still curious about one thing. . . How did you know we were on that train?'

'An educated guess.' He sat back in his seat. 'I phoned Lomond View to say I was coming back tomorrow morning, and when no one answered I was immediately suspicious. I'm afraid I simply put two and two together.'

He gave her a shrewd smile. 'You see, I know you. I know the sort of devious little things you get up to.

So I got straight into the car and headed south, hoping I could reach Carlisle before the train did. I knew the train wouldn't stop again until it reached London.'

'What a pity you made it.' Shiona smiled unsympathetically. 'That would've been quite a drive for you all the way to London. I reckon it would've taken you most of the night.'

She laid down her orange juice. 'But I'm still curious. How did you manage to persuade British Rail to allow you on to the train so you could drag me off?'

'I didn't drag you off, I merely escorted you. I'm sure they wouldn't have stood for any rough stuff.' He paused and shrugged. 'I simply told them that you were my wife and that you had taken all our money and our little girl and were running off to London to be with your lover.' He smiled a smug smile. 'They were most sympathetic. But though I say it myself, I spun them a pretty good story.'

'You devious devil!' Shiona laughed in spite of herself. 'What on earth must those men at the station have thought of me?'

Jake laughed with her. 'Not a lot, I'm afraid. I really laid your crimes on with a trowel.'

'I'll bet you did!' Her tone was teasing. 'No wonder they were giving me funny looks!'

He continued to smile across at her. 'Let that be a lesson.' Then, as the waitress arrived with Kirsty's and Shiona's orders, he glanced at the slim gold watch at his wrist. 'If you don't mind, I'd like to be on my way pretty soon. I'm expecting a couple of overseas phone calls at the house.' He paused. 'I can drop you off at Glasgow airport, if you like, or you can take a train to Prestwick and catch a plane from there.'

Shiona thought for only a moment. 'I'll fly from Prestwick.' She suspected it might be marginally quicker.

'OK, then I'll drop you off at the station.' He called to Kirsty. 'Come and eat your toast. They've brought your favourite brand of honey.'

Twenty minutes later they were on their way, the three of them piling into the big black Mercedes and heading back to the railway station.

Shiona stole a secret glance at Jake's profile. In a strange sort of way things felt easier between them. The anger and the hostility had quite gone from his manner, as though some kind of tacit truce had been reached.

And she had to confess, much as she hated to, that it felt nice to be on amicable terms with Jake. Perhaps, now that the air had been cleared between them, they might be able to achieve a state of understanding. Perhaps when she got back to Loch Lomond tomorrow they could sit down and discuss things in a civilised fashion.

Jake started to slow down as the station came in sight, and Shiona turned to him, pulling a face. 'I hope the same guys aren't there who were on duty last night. I don't think I could bear to look them in the face.'

He pulled into the forecourt. 'Don't worry, they won't be there. Their shift will have ended long ago.'

Shiona smiled. 'I certainly hope so.' Then she leaned into the back of the car to kiss Kirsty. 'I'll see you soon. Probably tomorrow. In the meantime, be a good girl.'

'I will be. 'Bye, Aunt Shiona.' As Shiona grabbed her bag and bade farewell to Jake, then hurried round the front of the car to the station entrance, the little girl leaned against the window and waved.

As Shiona paused to wave back, Jake's window buzzed open and suddenly he was leaning out slightly towards her. 'I wouldn't bother coming back,' he told her in a detached voice. 'It's a waste of your time and an annoyance to me. Just accept that you're beaten and stay away.'

Before she could answer, the window buzzed closed again and the big car was moving away from the kerb. And suddenly, for no reason, a pain went through her, as though he had reached out and driven a stake through her heart.

And in that moment she wished with every fibre of her being that it really was possible for her to stay away. Out of his reach. Where he couldn't hurt her. Where she need never think of him again.

She turned away stiffly. But she had no choice. For Kirsty's sake, she had to return.

CHAPTER SIX

'THANK heavens you're here!'

As she walked into the studio, a beaming Desmond rushed up to greet her. 'I've just had Henri on the line again, still being as hopelessly impossible as ever. He's threatening to fly back to Paris this evening unless he can fix up a meeting with you.'

Shiona took his arm as they headed for her office. 'Well, I'm here now, so he can see me whenever he likes.' She laughed good-naturedly and squeezed his arm. 'Come and fill me in over a cup of coffee.'

Twenty minutes later, after a diplomatic phone call, Shiona had succeeded in smoothing some of Henri's ruffled feathers. As she made a quick tour of the studio before dashing out to meet him, she was aware of a great sense of personal satisfaction.

It was so good to be among people who respected and admired her, and whom she admired and respected in return. After the past week at Loch Lomond, with Jake forever finding fault with her, it was like a dose of summer sunshine just to be accepted for what she was.

For she was far from being the ruthlessly manipulative monster that Jake appeared to have convinced himself she was. All she was was an extremely hardworking girl whose dreams and aspirations had, miraculously, been achieved. And achieved, what was more, almost entirely by her own efforts—even her stepfather had granted her that. For, unlike Jake, Douglas had never accused her of having cheated Ryan out of his fortune—in spite of the fact that, like the rest of the family, he had never known the tragic truth about his son.

Perhaps her mother had convinced him that Shiona was incapable of such behaviour, or perhaps he hadn't needed any convincing. He had always been kindly disposed towards his stepdaughter. Perhaps he had simply given her the benefit of the doubt.

Unlike Jake, who had always done the opposite. But then Jake seemed to take pleasure in believing the worst of her.

Shiona cast these thoughts from her as she hurried out to grab a taxi. Ahead of her lay an important business meeting. She must not allow thoughts of Jake to disturb her and upset her precious peace of mind.

But even as she deliberately shut him from her thoughts, it struck her with an icy sense of unease that over the past week something rather worrying had happened.

She had thought the time had gone when thoughts of Jake could upset her. But that, quite simply, was no longer so.

The meeting with Henri was a resounding success. Back at the studio three hours later Shiona told Desmond, 'The Paris gala is on! Henri has promised his full co-operation!'

'Congratulations! I knew you'd do it!' Desmond

subjected her to a spectacular hug. He glanced at his watch. 'Let's go and have a drink, then you can treat me to a celebratory dinner!'

'So, what are your plans?' he asked her later, as the waiter served them gâteaus from a sumptuous dessert trolley. 'Will you be staying around for a while, or going straight back to bonny Scotland?'

Shiona shook her head. 'Going straight back, I'm afraid. The custody hearing could be called at any time. I have to be there. I have to be on hand.'

'Do you think you can win?' Desmond's tone was sympathetic. 'I know how much that little girl means to you.'

Shiona shook her head. 'She means the world to me. That's why I've got to try, even though it looks hopeless. I can't let her fall into the hands of that awful woman.'

Desmond eyed her anguished face with sympathy. Then he took a bite of his passion cake and asked, 'How come Jake's marrying her if she's so awful? From what you've told me, he doesn't sound like anybody's fool.'

'Believe me, he's not. Anything but. But he never sees the awful side of her. When he's around she's all sweetness and light.'

'Have you told him what you've seen?'

'He wouldn't believe me. He'd think I was saying it out of spite.' She sat back in her seat. 'But perhaps the judge will believe me—and he's the one I really have to convince.'

Desmond reached out and laid a sympathetic hand

on her arm. 'I'm sure you can do it. You're a winner, Shiona. Whatever happens, just remember that.'

Shiona's plane touched down at Glasgow airport just a few minutes before midday the following day. Remembering that her car was still abandoned at Central Station, she took a taxi to where she had left it, and was relieved to find it still waiting there.

But as she drove out of the city, heading for the road bridge and the Kilpatrick Hills on the north bank of the Clyde, she could feel the tension in her tightening. Usually the familiar beauty of this place had the very opposite effect on her, but today as she headed towards Loch Lomond she was filled with a terrible sense of doom. By the time she finally headed south again Kirsty's future would have been decided. The thought made her stomach shrink inside her.

Instantly she chided herself. Be a little more positive! Remember what Desmond said. Remember you're a winner!

Just that thought made the energy surge through her. However hard she had to fight, she would make certain that Janice never became Kirsty's mother!

It was a great relief when she arrived at Lomond View to discover that the only person there was Inge, looking rosy-cheeked and happy after her few days' holiday. The thought of an immediate confrontation with Jake was not one which Shiona had been particularly relishing.

But she was a little worried when Inge told her, 'They haven't been back here, as far as I know. Mr MacKay phoned last night, just after I got in, to say that he and Kirsty were in Edinburgh and that they'd be staying there until further notice.'

Shiona bit back her anger. What was he playing at? Was this his way of paying her back for trying to sneak Kirsty down to London?

She put on a calm face. 'Well, whatever he said, he can't keep her away indefinitely. He has to bring her back for school on Monday. She's already missed a couple of days.'

But by Sunday evening there was still no sign of him, and no telephone call to explain what was happening. With difficulty Shiona resisted the urge to phone him up at home and demand an explanation. After all, he might be planning to bring Kirsty back on Monday morning, and there was no point in antagonising him unnecessarily.

When by Monday lunchtime there was still no word from him, however, she tried phoning him up at MacKay Contracting—only to be told that he was unavailable. The story was similar when she tried calling the house in desperation later that evening. 'Sorry, Mr MacKay can't be disturbed. If you'd like to leave a message, he'll get back to you.'

Needless to say, he did not get back to her. When Tuesday arrived Shiona was still in the dark. But not for much longer, she decided, her anger growing by the minute. Since he refuses to talk to me over the phone, he'll have the pleasure of talking to me in person instead!

She drove to Edinburgh in just over two hours, and headed for Jake's office, just off Princes Street, in the shadow of the capital's ancient, brooding castle. She parked her car and strode through the grand, carved doorway, her heels clicking purposefully as she headed for the reception desk.

'I've come to see Jake MacKay,' she told the girl at the desk, tossing back her mane of bright auburn hair.

The girl looked her up and down with curiosity. 'Do you have an appointment?' she enquired politely. 'Mr MacKay never sees anyone without an appointment.'

'Oh, don't worry, he'll see me. I'm his sister. And I'm here on urgent family business.'

As the girl raised a surprised eyebrow, Shiona smiled to herself. She had also surprised herself a little with her claim. It was the first time she had ever referred to herself as Jake's sister. She had never even referred to herself as his *stepsister* before! But then, she had never thought of him in a sisterly fashion. Unlike her attitude towards Ryan. She had been a true sister to Ryan.

The receptionist, still watching her, was phoning up to Jake's office. 'Your sister's here on urgent family business. She wants to see you right away.'

After a moment she laid the receiver down again, her surprise now turned to total bafflement. 'I'm sorry, he says he's too busy to see you.'

Shiona clenched her jaw. 'Does he indeed?' Then she was marching swiftly past the reception desk, heading for the lifts at the back of the hall. 'Well, he'll see me anyway!' she muttered to herself.

She had only ever visited his office once before— as an awestruck teenager in the company of her stepfather—but she remembered precisely where it was. On the top floor of the building, with a fine view of the castle.

As the lift doors opened and she stepped out into the corridor, it occurred to her that she must strike a very different figure from the wide-eyed girl who had made that first visit. Though her heart was thumping as it had then, no one but herself would ever know it. This time she appeared outwardly to be perfectly in control.

She strode through the door to the outer office of his sanctum, past his personal secretary, who blinked in astonishment. Then, without pausing for breath or breaking her stride, she pushed open the door of his private office.

Chin up, shoulders squared, she stepped into the room, and in a cool tone accused him, 'You don't look busy in the least. I'm sure you can spare me a few moments of your time.'

He was seated at his desk, his back to the window, so she could not see his expression clearly. But she didn't need to see it to sense the burning anger that poured from his eyes as he looked up at her.

'How dare you come barging in here like this? Who the hell do you think you are?'

Shiona never faltered. Her nervousness had vanished. She felt suddenly bold, on an adrenalin 'high'. With a mocking smile she lifted one eyebrow. 'Have you forgotten? I'm your sister.'

Jake had risen from his seat and was standing to face her. 'I thought I told you to stay in London? You should have taken my advice. I really don't want you here.'

'That's just too bad. I don't take orders from you. And I don't give a damn if you want me here or not. What's more. . .' she seated herself in one of the button-back chairs '. . . I won't be leaving until you've told me what I want to know.'

There was a click behind her as the office door opened. Shiona heard a soft female voice say, 'I'm sorry, sir. . .' Then, apologetically, 'Shall I bring you some coffee?'

He was about to say no. Shiona could sense it. She turned round sharply and addressed the secretary. 'I'd love some coffee. Black, please. No sugar.'

As she turned back to face Jake, his anger was tangible. He nodded to the secretary. 'Black for me, too.' Then, as the secretary retreated, he sat down in his chair again, laying his hands along the green leather arms. 'Why have you come back?' he demanded, scowling.

'I have unfinished business here.' She looked straight back at him and, smoothing the skirt of her blue wool suit, crossed her legs elegantly at the ankles. 'Don't tell me you'd forgotten that as well?'

He narrowed his eyes at her, then surprised her by smiling. 'Why did you tell Doreen, the downstairs receptionist, that you were my sister?' he enquired.

'Why, isn't it true?'

'Fortunately, no.'

'Stepsister, then.'

'If you insist. Though I must confess I'm rather

surprised that you should wish to claim any relationship at all with me.'

Shiona smiled thinly. 'Yes, it went against the
grain. However, my motives, I assure you, were
purely practical. I figured it might be useful for
gaining access.'

Jake shook his head at her. 'I'm sure no one
believed you. No girl could look less like my sister
than you do.'

'That doesn't mean anything. Siblings don't always
look alike. There are plenty that you would never
even guess were related.'

As soon as she'd said it, Shiona wished she hadn't.
She felt a sudden uncomfortable twist in her
stomach, and she could sense that Jake had felt the
same. What two siblings could have been less alike
than Jake and his very own brother, Ryan?

She bit her lip, watching his face for that familiar,
fleeting shadow of pain, which mention of Ryan
always brought to his features—and waiting, feeling
suddenly tense, for the bitter attack on her that
invariably followed it.

But just for once Jake refrained from attacking her,
though he held her eyes for a long, dangerous
moment. Then he lowered his gaze and observed
with dark humour, 'The receptionist probably
thought you were some irate girlfriend come to bring
me to book about something or other.'

Shiona frowned at him. 'And you about to be
married? Surely there are no irate girlfriends in your
life any more?'

She had caught him unawares. He seemed to shift

slightly, and his gaze became shuttered as he answered quickly, 'Absolutely not. I was merely posing a hypothesis.' He reached for the Caithness paperweight on his desk and fiddled with it absently for a moment. Then, as the office door opened, he seized the diversion.

'Ah, here you are with our coffee already.' He smiled at the secretary. 'Just what I'm needing.'

From beneath lowered lashes Shiona watched him in silence, as the secretary set out their cups of coffee before them. What on earth, she was wondering, had caused that un-Jake-like reaction?

She could tell that his remark about 'some irate girlfriend' had been spoken quite spontaneously, without thinking, as a joke. And though it had struck her as a slightly odd remark for a man on the brink of marriage to make, she most probably wouldn't have thought any more about it if he had responded to the way she had light-heartedly picked up on it with his usual unassailable self-assurance.

But he most definitely hadn't. He had seemed thrown for a moment, as though it had genuinely slipped his mind that he was about to be married. Shiona frowned to herself. How very peculiar. Scarcely what one expected from a man who was deeply in love.

And he was in love, surely? she asked herself, frowning. Why else would he be marrying Janice?

She had a sudden sharp memory of the unexpected sleeping arrangements during the weekend when Janice had stayed at Loch Lomond. It had struck her as strange that he had put Janice in the rose room, at the opposite end of the house to where he himself slept. Though she had no personal experience, she had always assumed that Jake would be a man of vigorous sexual appetites. And quite clearly, at least for the duration of that weekend, there had been no sexual activity between himself and his fiancée.

Was it possible, she wondered with a secret lift inside her, that his relationship with Janice was not all it seemed?

She was snapped out of her reverie as the door clicked shut and the secretary left them alone again. Jake sat back in his chair, his fingers toying with the glass paperweight, yet looking totally composed again, back to his old self.

The blue eyes regarded her across the stretch of mahogany desk. 'So, now that you're here, you'd better tell me what you've come for.'

'I think you know what I've come for.' Shiona's eyes narrowed. 'I've come to find out what you've done with Kirsty—and when you intend returning her to Lomond View.'

Jake lifted up the paperweight and let it rest in his palm, his eyes seeming to examine it as he responded, 'The first part of your question is easy to answer. Kirsty is currently staying with me. As to the second part. . .' He shrugged and raised his eyes to meet Shiona's. 'I'm afraid it's impossible for me to give you a definite answer.' He smiled infuriatingly. 'Let's just say that Kirsty will be staying where she is until I see fit to return her.'

Shiona clenched her jaw, her irritation rising. 'How typically high-handed of you,' she replied, her tone glacial. 'Has it slipped your mind that the child has to go to school?'

'High-handed?' He smiled. 'That's good coming from you. At least my action is within the law.'

'I sincerely doubt that.' She let the rebuke slide over her. 'I think you'll find that it's a legal require-ment in Scotland that a child be provided with an education.'

'There are schools in Edinburgh.' He regarded her harshly. 'And since she will eventually be coming to live here anyway, don't you think she may as well make the change-over now?'

'No, I'm afraid I don't!' Shiona's eyes were glitter-ing. 'How can you be so utterly selfish as to uproot the child from her home and school at this stage, when nothing has been finally decided by the court? What if I win? Have you thought of that? What if she has to be uprooted all over again, just as she's getting used to her new school?'

She paused for breath as a sudden thought occurred to her, then leaned forward in her seat, her eyes accusing. 'Perhaps that's why you're doing it? To strengthen your case. You're going to present the court with a *fait accompli* to try and persuade them to rule in your favour!'

'They'll rule in my favour anyway.' Jake's tone was dismissive. 'I don't have to resort to such underhand tricks.'

'So you admit it's underhand? Underhand and selfish! I actually thought you cared about Kirsty. Now I know just how wrong I was!'

Jake watched her for a moment, then observed in

a soft voice, 'Of course, I care about Kirsty. I care very much.' Then, before she could answer, he leaned back in his chair and dropped the paper-weight on to the desk. 'That's why I'm keeping her at my place for the moment.' He raised his eyes sharply. 'Until she's recovered from her flu.'

Shiona felt momentarily stunned. She blinked at him owlishly. 'Flu?' she repeated. 'You mean Kirsty has flu?'

'That's what I said.' His tone was acid. 'She started shivering and sneezing soon after we left Carlisle. Considering there was no one to look after her at Lomond View, I decided that the best place for her was with me.'

Shiona swallowed. 'And who's looking after her at your place?'

'Me, when I'm there. But for the most part Mrs Aitken, my live-in housekeeper. Kirsty knows her well and they're very fond of each other. You don't have to worry, she's in excellent hands.'

Shiona glanced away, her eyes dropping to her lap. Suddenly she felt quite overcome with shame to think that Kirsty's illness might be all her fault. If she hadn't subjected her to that late-night journey, with all the upheavals that had accompanied it, perhaps the poor child would not have fallen ill.

'I imagine she caught the bug from someone in her class at school. I understand there's quite a bit of it going around.' Jake fingered the paperweight idly as he continued, 'It had probably been developing for a few days. I suspect that wherever she'd been—on a train to London or at home at Lomond View—it wouldn't have made the slightest bit of difference. It was bound to knock her under, sooner or later.'

It was as though he had read into her mind and gone out of his way to reassure her. Shiona looked across at him, touched by his kindness, and more than a little bewildered by it, too. It was so unexpected. So unlike him.

'I suppose you're right,' she answered gratefully.

He reached for the paperweight and weighed it in his hand again. 'She's already much better, I'm happy to tell you. She's a strong little character, and she's a fighter. In a couple of days she'll be up and about again, but I've been told by the doctor to keep her off school for a while longer. Not that she's complaining about that, of course.'

Shiona smiled. 'Yes, I'll bet.' And inwardly she thanked fate that, after all, Jake had stopped them on their flight to London. If Kirsty had fallen ill once they were down in London she would have been forced to stay there until she'd recovered—and then she would have been in serious trouble, not only with Jake but with the law as well.

She cleared her throat. 'Once she's recovered, you will be bringing her back to Lomond View?'

'Of course. For the moment that's her home. And, as you so responsibly pointed out just a moment ago, that is also where her school is. I'll be taking her back as soon as she's well.'

'I see.' Shiona hesitated for a moment. 'If you don't mind, I'd like to see her before then. Would you object to my paying her a visit?'

He did not answer immediately. Perhaps he would say no. Shiona steeled herself for disappointment.

But instead he answered, 'That would depend.'

'Depend on what?'

'On your intentions.'

'What do you mean?'

'I mean, my dear Shiona, that I must have your absolute assurance that you don't intend trying to spirit her away again.'

'Of course I don't! What do you take me for?' Shiona bit her lip. 'You have my assurance. Absolutely. Unconditionally. I wouldn't dream of doing such a thing.'

Jake dropped the heavy paperweight into the palm of his other hand, his eyes never leaving hers as he did so. 'OK, I'll believe you. For once, I'll trust you. But pity help you if you let me down.'

'I won't.' She felt a dart go through her. What an abysmally low opinion he had of her—and, unexpectedly, that reminder hurt. She held his eyes carefully. 'You can trust me.'

He nodded. 'We shall see.' Then he straightened suddenly and returned the paperweight to its place on his desk. 'You can see her this evening, since you've already made the journey. You can come with me when I leave the office.'

'That would be great! Thank you,' Shiona answered. Then a thought occurred to her. 'That's going to be rather late. By the time we get to your place it'll almost be Kirsty's bedtime. I'd like to spend a little more time with her than that.'

'So stay overnight and spend time with her

tomorrow. That's no problem. There's plenty of room.'

Shiona hesitated, surprised by the invitation, and for some reason assailed by an anxious tightening in her stomach at the thought of staying overnight at Jake's house.

How utterly ridiculous! she chided herself sharply. We've spent dozens of nights under the same roof in the past!

'OK,' she answered, not quite looking at him. Then, on a practical note, she enquired, 'What time do you leave the office?'

'Pretty late, usually. Never before six.' Then, as her face fell, he added, 'However, since Kirsty's been staying with me I've made a point of packing up just after five.' He glanced at his watch. 'It's just gone three now. Can you amuse yourself for a couple of hours?'

'Easily.' Shiona rose to her feet.

'Of course. I'd forgotten.' He deliberately met her eyes. 'You'll have no problem at all filling in a couple of hours with all the Princes Street shops to keep you occupied. Spending money, after all, is one of your favourite pastimes.'

It was yet another dig, and again Shiona felt it bruise her. As Jake started to come round the desk towards her, she turned away, averting her eyes. What was happening to her? Her immunity was crumbling. She was becoming almost as sensitive to him as she had been all those years ago.

On long strides he was leading her towards the door, oblivious to her inner anguish. 'Wait for me downstairs in Reception. I'll be there as soon after five as I can make it.'

He held the door open for her, and she stepped quickly through it. Then as she muttered, 'Goodbye,' he warned in a clipped tone,

'Make sure you're waiting. If you get carried away with your shopping and turn up late, I won't hang around, I'll just leave without you.'

'Thanks for the warning.' Shiona turned to meet his eyes, hating the way her heart was still beating so fast. Then she turned smartly on her heel and marched out of the door.

CHAPTER SEVEN

IN FACT, Shiona very nearly didn't make it in time. She'd been browsing in a bookshop after buying a bedtime book for Kirsty when she'd suddenly caught sight of the clock on the wall and seen, to her horror, that it was nearly five o'clock.

She smiled to herself now as she drove through the outskirts of Edinburgh, eyes fixed like limpets on the black Mercedes in front of her—if she lost sight of Jake now, she was done for! She would never find her way to his house on her own!—and recalled her headlong flight down Princes Street and her breathless arrival back at MacKay Contracting.

'Has Mr MacKay left yet?' she'd enquired of the startled receptionist. It wouldn't have surprised her in the slightest if he'd left a few minutes early, just for the pleasure of leaving her stranded.

But the girl had shaken her head. 'No, not yet.' And, with a thankful sigh, Shiona had sunk down on one of the sofas in the reception area. 'That was a close one!' she'd muttered to herself.

In fact, he didn't appear till almost twenty-past, by which time Shiona had managed to catch her breath and run a surreptitious comb through her wild mane of hair.

As he stepped out of the elevator and strode towards her, she felt her heartbeat do a funny little dance. He looked so tall, so strikingly handsome in the deep blue suit and immaculate white shirt. The hero of her dreams of all those years ago, those dreams that she had never quite forgotten.

She checked the thought instantly. She had taken leave of her senses! Of course she had forgotten them! They were dead and buried! Something must have short-circuited in her brain!

'So you made it.' He smiled a fleeting smile, carefully surveying her as she rose to her feet. 'But where are all your packages?' he asked. 'Have you hidden them in your car?'

Did he never grow tired of making these accusations?

'I don't have any packages,' she informed him tightly. 'All I've bought is a toothbrush for myself and a story book for Kirsty.' She paused an instant. 'You're forgetting,' she reminded him, 'it's only other people's money that I enjoy spending.'

'So it is.' His eyes surveyed her for a moment. Then, almost impatiently, he turned on his heel. 'Let's get moving before the traffic gets jammed up. It can be pretty horrendous at this time of the evening.'

He hadn't been joking, Shiona observed to herself now, as she followed his tail out on to the road to Balerno. The rush-hour traffic in the city centre had been as thick as a plate of home-made porridge! Yet Jake had negotiated it with skill and creativity, darting up side-roads to avoid the congestion and taking clever detours that saved both temper and time. It had felt like a game of hide-and-seek, and Shiona, though at times she had been terrified of losing him, had thoroughly enjoyed the drive.

And now they had left the city behind and were heading out into the open country. Shiona felt a tiny tremor of excitement. She had never visited Jake's home before.

It appeared quite suddenly as they turned a sharp bend, an imposing stone edifice with ivy-clad walls, set among tall poplars, well back from the road. And somehow she didn't need to be told they had arrived. It was precisely the sort of place where she had always imagined he would live.

They turned in through a pair of eagle-mounted gateposts, then at the end of a long driveway at last drew to a halt. Shiona climbed out on to the crunchy, gravelled forecourt and looked around her.

'It's beautiful,' she said.

He seemed not to have heard her, and in a way she was grateful. It had not been her intention to favour him with a compliment. The observation had simply slipped out.

'This way,' he was instructing, leading her on brisk strides up the double stone staircase that led to the front door. As they reached the top the door opened magically and a beaming, plump-faced woman was waiting to greet them.

'Welcome home, Mr MacKay.' The woman grinned at Shiona. 'I see you've got a visitor with you.'

As they stepped into the hallway, Jake introduced them. 'Shiona, this is Mrs Aitken, my most able and valued housekeeper. Mrs Aitken, meet Shiona

Fergusson, Kirsty's half-sister. She'll be spending the night here.'

Mrs Aitken beamed at her. 'So *you're* Aunt Shiona! I've heard so much about you, you wouldn't believe it. Kirsty will be fair delighted to see you!'

Shiona's cheeks turned pink with pleasure. 'How is she?' she asked, barely covering her delight.

'Much better today. She's got her appetite back.' The plump-faced woman turned to Jake now. 'I gave her some poached chicken breast at lunchtime and she even managed a couple of scones for tea.'

'Well done.' Jake smiled at her. 'You're doing a good job.' Then he glanced fleetingly at Shiona before heading for the staircase. 'I suggest we go up and see her now.'

They stayed with Kirsty for just under an hour, and it was a relief to Shiona to see how well she was looking. She had obviously been well cared for throughout her illness—but then, Shiona had never for one moment doubted that.

When it was time for 'lights out', she and Jake left the room together, and out in the corridor Jake told her, 'Mrs Aitken usually serves supper about eight, so if you want to freshen up you have a bit of time. I'm going to have a shower. I'll show you where your room is.'

'Thanks,' Shiona nodded, suddenly feeling awkward to be alone in his company without a third person. She shook herself mentally. What a silly thing to feel!

A moment later, with a curt 'Follow me', he was

leading her down to the end of the corridor, then along a short passageway off to the right.

'Here we are.' He pushed one of the doors open and invited her to enter the pretty pink and white room.

'You have your own bathroom.' He pointed vaguely. 'I think you should find everything you need. If there are any problems just call down to Mrs Aitken. There's an internal phone there by the bed.'

Once he had gone, Shiona sank down on to the bed and kicked off her shoes, glad to be alone for a few minutes. She leaned back against the pillows and looked around her. Here in Jake's splendid and tastefully furnished home was the very last place she had expected to be tonight. In fact, a lot of unexpected things had happened today.

She had a sudden sharp recall of that moment in Jake's office when he had revealed his strange lack of commitment to Janice. And the more she thought about it the more she felt certain that her instinctive deduction had been right. Whatever else he was, he was not in love with Janice—unless that moment in his office had been a mere innocent slip.

It could have been, she told herself doubtfully. These things could happen, after all—even to men as unprone to making slips as Jake! But something was telling her it was no slip—and then, in a blinding flash, she knew!

She sat up, her heart racing. He wasn't in love with Janice! He was, after all, simply marrying her in order to gain guardianship of Kirsty!

Suddenly she was assailed by a tangle of emotions,

not least among them a silly sense of relief that she knew was totally out of place. Why should she care whether he was in love or not?

She also felt shock that he should actually be capable of such an utterly cynical act. Would he have been prepared to marry anyone who would have him just to keep Kirsty out of her hands? Did he really know what type of woman Janice was? Didn't it matter to him that she was only after his money, that she was far from being the warm, motherly soul that she seemed?

But her instincts told her no. He adored little Kirsty. There was no way in the world that he would deliberately inflict on her a woman who was unsuitable to be her mother.

Shiona jumped to her feet, the adrenalin racing through her. She must waste no time in putting him right. At the first opportunity she must tell him what she knew. And, perhaps, since he was not blinded by love after all, he might be prepared to listen to her for once!

Fifteen minutes later, after a lightning shower, and dressed once more in her cream suit and silk blouse, Shiona hurried downstairs to join Jake in the drawing-room.

He was standing by the drinks table, pouring himself a measure of neat whisky, when she walked into the room. 'I was expecting to have dinner with a client this evening, but the appointment has been unexpectedly cancelled.' He flicked her a glance. 'So it looks, after all, as though you and I will be dining together.'

She couldn't resist it. 'You must be overjoyed.' Quite the opposite had been evident from his tone of voice.

He smiled a dry smile. 'I expect I'll survive it.' Then, watching her, he took a mouthful of his drink. 'Just so long as you're not planning any physical attacks on me this evening. . . I'd prefer not to have any cups of coffee thrown in my face.'

Shiona had almost forgotten that unfortunate incident. 'I shall try to control myself.' She met his mocking gaze, noting that in spite of the typical little dig there was less malice than usual in his manner. Perhaps he was trying to be hospitable—not an easy task for him when she was the guest!

At any rate, he was looking relaxed, dressed in beige trousers and a deep blue sweatshirt, and the informality of his attire suited him, Shiona thought. The soft lines of the sweatshirt that moulded the broad shoulders gave him an air of easy, masculine power, and the blue almost exactly matched the blue of his eyes.

Shiona stopped herself short. She was doing it again! Reacting to him physically, just as she used to all those years ago. And it really was quite out of place!

She drew herself up, stilling her racing pulses, as he asked her now with a wave at the drinks table, 'Would you care to indulge in a drink before dinner?'

'Yes, thanks. I'd like a Dubonnet.' She cleared her throat. 'With just a splash of lemonade.'

'Ice?' he enquired, as he reached for a glass and Shiona seated herself in one of the armchairs.

'Yes, please,' she nodded, taking care not to look at him. Even now she had not entirely recovered herself.

He came towards her and held out her glass to her, then seated himself in one of the armchairs opposite. 'Dinner will be ready in about fifteen minutes. I hope you're hungry?' he offered, watching her.

'I'm absolutely starving.' Though her voice sounded normal, Shiona was aware that she was feeling awkward again, just as she had when they were upstairs earlier. It was a new sensation, and she didn't like it in the slightest. She took a mouthful of her drink and pulled herself together. 'I haven't had a bite to eat since breakfast.'

'Mrs Aitken will be pleased.' Jake smiled fleetingly, an affectionate smile that softened his features. 'I got the impression that something major was happening in the kitchen. She appears to be going to a bit of trouble in your honour.'

'That's very kind of her, but quite unnecessary.' Shiona found herself watching his softened features with a feeling almost of secret envy. He was capable of such thoughtfulness and generosity towards others. It was only towards herself that she'd ever seen him act meanly.

She squashed the thought. It made her feel vulnerable, the way she always used to feel in the past. And she did not want to start feeling that way again.

Just concentrate on watching out for the right opportunity to broach the subject of Janice, she reminded herself. That's the only thought that need occupy you this evening!

She sat back in her seat and glanced around her. 'This is a very nice place you have here,' she told him. Perhaps flattery might please him and soften his mood further. The more malleable he was the better for her!

'I'm glad you like it.' He did not appear flattered. 'Personally, I find it very much to my taste.'

'I love all the little knick-knacks.' Shiona continued to glance round her. 'These beautiful lamps and lovely ornaments. . .' Her gaze fell on the Baccarat crystal pyramid on the glass-topped side table at her elbow. 'This is beautiful,' she enthused. 'So simple, yet so striking——' And then her breath caught in her throat as though someone had kicked her. Her voice trailed off. Her heart was pounding.

Although she did not look at Jake, she could feel he was watching her and that he knew what had stopped her dead in her tracks. And try as she might she could not detach her eyes from the object on the table that had so totally winded her.

Then she heard Jake speak. 'It's a good likeness, isn't it? It was taken just before his twenty-first birthday.'

'I know. I remember.' Shiona swallowed drily, her fingers clutched tightly around her glass as she continued to stare with unblinking, blurred vision at the photograph of Ryan in the big silver frame.

'But then, Ryan always did take a very good photograph.' There was an edge to Jake's voice now, an edge of hostility, that caused her to turn round and look him in the face.

But she could not say a word as he went on in that same tone.

'You say you can remember that photograph being taken. It was a very happy day, I seem to remember.' Then, as she nodded in agreement, he added viciously, 'Were you already planning, even as that photograph was being taken, how you were going to fleece him of every penny he possessed?'

Shiona felt her blood go cold. She felt like jumping from her seat and running from the room. She could not bear to listen to his accusations. But her limbs were paralysed. She was glued to the cushions. She stared back at him miserably. 'No,' she answered numbly.

'That came later, did it? Once you were down in London?' He leaned back in his armchair and regarded her harshly. 'I've always been curious to know how you did it. . . Did you have some master plan or did you just plan it bit by bit?'

The anger in his face was like a wall between them. A wall that bristled with bayonets and barbed wire.

Shiona took a deep breath. 'I don't blame you for being angry, believing what you do about me. I know you loved Ryan and that you always stood by him. But I loved him, too. I was never his enemy.'

'Then what were you?' Jake's blue eyes flayed her and she could sense the pain that shimmered in his voice. 'Most certainly you were not his friend. In my book friends don't rob one another.'

'Nor in mine. I never robbed your brother.'

'You mean what he gave he gave to you freely?' His tone was scathing. 'That makes all the difference! And in return, no doubt, you gave him a good time in bed!'

'I gave him nothing of the sort!'

'Oh, not even that? Poor Ryan!' His mouth twisted. 'He really got a rotten deal!'

To have to sit there and take his abuse was like being bound hand and foot to a torturer's chair. Shiona longed to yell, Stop!, and pour out the truth and see the rage and the pain and the hatred of her finally and forever erased from his face.

But she could not. All she could say was, 'You're horribly wrong. I loved your brother. I would never have harmed him.'

It was a relief when a couple of minutes later, amidst the deafening silence that had descended on the room, Mrs Aitken poked her head round the door. 'Dinner will be served whenever you're ready.'

'We're ready now.' Jake rose to his feet, smiling, throwing off his anger like a mantle. He even managed a civil glance at Shiona. 'Shall we go through? We don't want dinner to spoil.'

He'd been right about Mrs Aitken having gone to some trouble. That was evident the moment they stepped into the dining-room. The table was laid out fit for a king, all gleaming silver and twinkling crystal. And the meal that followed was a veritable banquet.

There was fresh salmon to start with, baked in a light-as-a-feather pastry, then duck cooked in a mouth-watering loganberry sauce, plus a couple of huge tureens of fresh vegetables and plenty of white wine to wash down each delicious mouthful.

And as the meal progressed the atmosphere between them lightened. The subject of Ryan was mercifully dropped, and for once Jake appeared to be as anxious as Shiona was to avoid any further confrontation.

They spoke of nothing in particular—holidays, films—and by the time Mrs Aitken appeared in the doorway, carrying aloft a flaming baked Alaska, the tension in Shiona had all but vanished. To her astonishment, she had almost enjoyed their conversation. Its very normality had been something of a novelty!

But what was still troubling her was the fact that she had still not broached the subject of Janice.

Surreptitiously now, she glanced across at his profile as Mrs Aitken piled baked Alaska on to each of their plates. Would he listen to her when she told him the truth about Janice? Would she be able to persuade him that he was making a mistake? One way or the other she would find out soon enough, for she must definitely speak up before the meal was over.

As Mrs Aitken left, Shiona braced herself. What she had to say must be handled with delicacy. She must tell him what she knew about Janice without alienating him. He must be made to realise that she was speaking up for Kirsty's sake, that she was not motivated by personal spite.

But how to begin? She eyed him cautiously. He

was like a tinder-box where she was concerned. One wrong move and he would be up in flames.

As though he were telepathic, he raised his eyes to look at her. Shiona sensed that he knew she had something on her mind. But he did not prompt her. On the contrary. He simply turned his attention back to his pudding.

She cleared her throat and took a deep breath. 'Jake, there's something I'd like to discuss with you.'

He took a mouthful of his pudding. 'And what might that be?'

She cleared her throat again. 'It's about Janice,' she said.

'Janice?'

'Yes, Janice. Your fiancée.'

He smiled. 'Yes, I do know who she is. What do you want to discuss about her?'

This was the hard part. Shiona laid down her spoon. 'I don't think she'd make a suitable mother for Kirsty.'

Blue eyes met hers candidly. 'Yes, I know,' he said.

'You mean you agree with me?' Shiona was astounded. 'Then why——?'

'What I mean is that you have already told me,' he cut in sharply. 'You need not repeat yourself.'

'But I haven't told you why. I have good reason. I believe you're making a terrible mistake.'

His eyes had grown ice-cold. 'Is that so? Well, perhaps I'm not interested in what you believe.'

'You ought to be!' Damn his arrogance! 'Our little sister's future is at stake!'

His eyes looked right through her. 'Don't you mean *your* future? That's the only future *you* care about!'

Shiona counted to ten. 'You're wrong about that! You're wrong about me and you're wrong about Janice!'

He shook his head. 'Oh, no, my dear Shiona, I fear I have never been wrong about you. Alas, over the years I have become far too familiar with your greedy, grasping little ways.'

'That's almost funny!' Shiona laughed harshly. 'But the one with the greedy, grasping little ways happens to be your fiancée, not me!'

It was his turn to laugh harshly. 'Go and tell that to Ryan! I'm sure, if he were alive, he'd find that most reassuring!'

The mention of Ryan almost silenced her. She felt that familiar wave of nausea wash through her. But as she looked into Jake's face and his condemning blue eyes she was overcome by a rush of indignation. He had hurt her enough with his false accusations. It was time she did a bit of hurting, too.

She narrowed her eyes and threw the cruel truth at him. 'I don't know why you think she's marrying you. Maybe you're fool enough to believe she loves you. But she doesn't love you. She doesn't even care for you. The only reason she's marrying you is to get her hands on your money!'

To her chagrin he did not look hurt in the slightest. His expression remained flinty and quite unreadable.

'No doubt you feel better now you've got that off your chest.'

Damn his composure! Shiona clenched her fists beneath the table and continued to glare across at him with ferociously narrowed eyes. 'But, of course, I'm forgetting. . .' Her tone was lethal. 'You don't care that she's not in love with you because you're not the least bit in love with her, either!'

'Is that what you think?'

'That's what I think!'

'Well, do you know what *I* think?' He leaned across the table towards her. 'I think that my relationship with Janice is really none of your damned business!'

'Oh, but you're wrong! Your relationship with Janice happens to be very much my damned business, particularly now that I understand the truth!'

'*You*, understand the truth? I very much doubt it. For you the truth is simply something you invent.'

Shiona shook her head. 'No, that's your game! *You're* the one who's inventing the truth!'

'And what am I inventing?' His tone was jagged. 'Please be so good as to enlighten me.'

'What you're inventing is a whole false little scenario of supposedly future wedded bliss, just so you can win custody of Kirsty. Well, I know what you're up to and I've tumbled to Janice. She's nothing but a mercenary little gold-digger, and I will not allow her to be a mother to my sister!'

Jake's eyes had narrowed to pinpoints. 'A gold-digger, is she? Well, I suppose it takes one to know one, as they say!' He pushed aside his plate. 'But don't think you can fool me. I know exactly what you're up to. . .' He held her eyes a moment. 'But you'll never win custody. That is something I can guarantee!'

'What a pity it's not for you to guarantee! The ultimate decision will be taken by the court—and, don't worry, I shall make very sure that they know precisely what type of person Janice really is. Not the type of person to be Kirsty's mother.' She glared across at him. 'And if you really loved Kirsty like you say you do, you would realise that for yourself!'

'Don't you worry about Kirsty!' He pushed back his chair, the gesture violent, making the chair topple. 'I shall see to it that she doesn't end up in the wrong hands. Never doubt that for a minute.'

As he rose to his feet, Shiona glanced up at him. 'You mean you'll reconsider your marriage to Janice?'

His eyes scowled down at her. 'I mean what I said. I will never allow Kirsty to fall into the wrong hands. And the worst possible hands she could fall into are yours!'

Then, with a final black glance at her, he stepped away from the table and swept like a tornado through the dining-room door.

Next morning Shiona remained in bed until she was certain that Jake had left for the office.

She stared at the ceiling. So, they had come to this. They were about to become locked in a bitter legal battle for the future of the child they both loved.

It was totally wrong. It mustn't happen. Kirsty's future mustn't be decided in such a way.

Through her anger and frustration there was another emotion, too. A sense of deep and profound

disappointment. As long as she had believed that
Jake had no suspicion of what type of woman Janice
really was, she had been able to forgive his cynical
marriage. But last night he had refused even to
consider what she had told him, tossing it to one side
as though it didn't matter.

Either he loved Kirsty less than she had given him
credit for, or he hated Shiona even more fiercely than
she had ever suspected.

She sensed the truth was undoubtedly the latter,
and it was like a lance driving through her. If only he
knew he had no cause to hate her. If only she could
tell him the truth.

Could she? she wondered. And, more appropri-
ately, *should* she?

She turned the possibility round and round in her
head. If it might benefit Kirsty for him to know what
had really happened between herself and Ryan,
would she be justified in breaking her promise? For,
once he knew the truth, he could no longer believe
that she was the monster he had branded her, and
that might lead him to abandon his marriage, whose
only purpose, she was certain now, was to thwart
her.

Surely, she reasoned, the future of a child was
more important than a promise to a man who was
now dead?

Yet it was a hard decision. She had promised Ryan
faithfully. And yet the only alternative was to sacri-
fice Kirsty. Even Ryan, she felt certain, would not
have wanted that.

But at last she came to a painful decision. She got

up, showered quickly, and pulled on her clothes. I shall go to his office and tell him, she decided. This afternoon. Before I change my mind.

Kirsty was still sound asleep, she discovered, when she poked her head round the little girl's door. So she hurried downstairs to fix herself some breakfast—and almost stopped in her tracks at the sight of the figure who was seated at the kitchen table.

'Janice?' She blinked. 'What are you doing here?'

Janice laid down her coffee-cup with equal surprise. 'I could ask the same thing of you,' she countered crisply.

Not much sign, Shiona observed, of the good-natured warmth and motherly charm that was so much in evidence when Jake was around!

'I was visiting Kirsty,' she answered flatly. Then she added, 'I spent the night here,' hoping to annoy her.

She sensed that she had. Janice's hard eyes glinted. Then she seemed to shrug as though it really didn't matter.

'I came to see Jake.' She picked up her cup again. 'But Mrs Aitken told me I'd just missed him, so I got her to make me a cup of coffee.'

I'll just bet you did! Shiona thought disapprovingly, as she crossed to the coffee-maker to switch it on for herself. I can just imagine you bossing poor Mrs Aitken around!

She glanced at Janice over her shoulder. 'How come you're not at work today?'

There was a momentary pause as Janice drank her coffee. Then she laid her cup down on her saucer with a click. 'I have the morning off.' She paused another moment, as though ensuring that she had Shiona's full attention. Then she added in an oddly tantalising tone, 'Today's my morning at the hospital.'

Shiona turned to look at her. 'Hospital?' she repeated. And, in spite of her dislike, her tone was sympathetic. In no way did she wish ill health on the woman.

'Hospital. That's right.' Janice smiled a strange smile. Then, feigning coyness, she fluttered her lashes. 'I suppose I can tell you. I was at the antenatal clinic. It's supposed to be a secret, but I'm pregnant.'

Shiona was unaware that her jaw had dropped open. 'Pregnant?' she repeated. 'Pregnant? You?'

Janice nodded. 'Rather silly of me, wasn't it, to go and make such a careless mistake?'

Shiona felt as though a bomb had gone off in her face. She swallowed drily. 'It can happen to anyone.' She was vaguely aware that she ought to offer congratulations, but for some reason she didn't feel in a congratulatory frame of mind.

Janice started to stand up. 'I'd better go now. My appointment at the hospital's in half an hour, and sometimes the traffic can be just deadly.'

Suddenly there was a triumphant little lift to her chin. She knew her news had left her audience speechless.

Out of politeness Shiona escorted Janice to the door, then stood in the doorway to watch her drive off. It was all clear now—why Jake was marrying Janice in spite of the lack of love between them. And it was such an obvious explanation that she ought to have thought of it herself, but for some reason it had never for one moment crossed her mind.

Naïve fool, she thought, staring into space, fighting back the emotions that threatened to swamp her. For all at once she could feel sweeping in on her a sense of utter desolation, the like of which she hadn't known for years.

CHAPTER EIGHT

AFTER Janice had gone Shiona went back inside and sat down at the kitchen table with a cup of strong black coffee.

What a mess, she was thinking. What a total jumble. With every corner she turned things seemed to grow more tangled. It would be futile now to think of trying to persuade Jake to rethink his intended marriage to Janice. How could he do that when she was carrying his child? He really had very little choice in the matter.

Carrying Jake's child.

The words seized her by the throat. She squeezed her eyes shut and clenched her fists tight. She was jealous, she realised. Bitterly jealous. Yet how could she possibly feel jealous over a man whom she had so long ago evicted from her heart?

As she took a mouthful of her coffee, her hands were shaking. What a fool she was. What a perfect idiot. She was feeling exactly as she had in the old days. Heartsore and vulnerable and sick with misery.

She gave herself a shake. Snap out of it! she commanded. It isn't really you who's feeling this way, it's the girl you used to be who's been somehow resurrected—brought back to life by all the memories that surround you. And you mustn't allow her to take over your emotions. You must put a stop to her before she destroys you.

Abruptly, she stood up. Nothing would destroy her—least of all these totally inappropriate emotions for a man who had brought her nothing but misery. Surely she had more pride than that?

She let out her breath, stilling the trembling within her. I shall go and get ready, then drive into Edinburgh and finally tell Jake the truth about Ryan. If he has to marry Janice, that's his misfortune, but I shall force him to see that if he really loves Kirsty he won't force her to share his fate. I shall convince him that Kirsty would be better off with me.

Steeled with resolve, Shiona felt much better. Head high, she hurried upstairs to change.

Alas, Shiona's plans were destined to be thwarted.

She arrived at Jake's office shortly after ten to be told by his secretary, 'He's not here, I'm afraid. He's gone to a meeting at Cambuslang. I don't expect him back until mid-afternoon.'

Shiona cursed her luck. 'Then I'll come back after lunch. In the meantime, if you hear from him, please tell him I need to see him urgently.'

The girl glanced up at her. 'You're his sister, is that right?'

'In a manner of speaking. We're not blood-related. Just tell him it's Miss Fergusson who needs to see him.'

As she turned away, she felt a small surge of triumph. Already she had put a little distance between them!

But the day dragged on with still no sign of Jake. She'd been waiting outside his office for the best part of three hours when his secretary came to tell her that he'd just phoned in.

'The meeting's been extended. He won't be back today—at least, not to the office; he'll be going straight home.'

'Did you tell him I was here?'

'I told him, Miss Fergusson. He said to please meet him back at the house this evening.'

Did he indeed? How uncommonly civil of him to make such a co-operative and hospitable offer! But though she was anxious to see him, Shiona had no desire to end up spending another night under his roof.

She rose to her feet. 'If he calls in again, please tell him I'll come back to the office tomorrow morning. I'm going back to Loch Lomond now. If he wants to, he can reach me there.'

Shiona took the long way back to Loch Lomond, via Perth and Comrie and Loch Earn, stopping for a meal at a wayside hotel, then heading south via Glen Dochart just after nine o'clock.

She felt edgy and unsettled, dreading tomorrow and the final show-down over Ryan—for the prospect of breaking her solemn promise to him still lay heavily on her mind.

But there was no other way, she kept reassuring herself. For Kirsty's sake, she had to clear her name.

The sitting-room light at Lomond View was on as usual as she turned into the darkened driveway. Nettie always left it on, even when no one was at home and she herself had retired to her own rooms for the evening and Inge was out, as was the case tonight.

Shiona parked at the front, instead of at the side of the house where everyone normally parked their cars, and, pushing back her hair, headed for the front door.

A quick bath and bed, she promised herself, sighing, as she stuck her key into the front door lock. All at once, she felt desperately tired.

But as she stepped into the hall she knew something was wrong. With all her instincts she could sense it.

She frowned and looked around her. 'Nettie?' she called out. 'Nettie! Are you there?'

'Nettie's gone to bed.'

Shiona jumped and spun round, startled, as a voice spoke from the drawing-room doorway behind her. Then, as she saw who it was, her stomach tightened.

'What the devil are *you* doing here?'

Jake leaned against the doorway, blue eyes narrowed, an inscrutable expression on his face. 'I thought my secretary told you to meet me at the house in Edinburgh? Why do you always force me to go chasing after you?'

What was he talking about? 'Chasing after me? I told your secretary I would see you tomorrow. What I wanted to see you about isn't *that* urgent.'

'I didn't get that message.' There was a troubled air about him. He had the look of a man who'd been pacing about restlessly, his tie loose about his throat, his shirt collar undone. Even his hair was distinctly ruffled, as though impatient fingers had been frequently run through it.

He let out his breath sharply. 'When you weren't at the house I came straight here.' He glanced at his watch. 'I've been waiting for two hours.'

She almost apologised, but in time she stopped herself. 'It really wasn't necessary for you to go to all that trouble. What I have to say to you could have waited till tomorrow.'

Besides, she was thinking, what on earth had possessed him to come rushing over here just because she wanted to see him? But then, in his next breath, he enlightened her.

'But I'm afraid what *I* have to say to *you* couldn't wait.' There was a grim expression about his mouth as he said it. The narrowed blue eyes seemed to pierce right through her. 'I've come to talk to you about Ryan.'

'Ryan?' Shiona blinked at him. Had the world gone crazy? 'I don't understand.' She frowned across the hall at him. 'It was precisely about Ryan that I wanted to talk to you.'

One cynical eyebrow lifted. 'What a coincidence.' Then he shifted impatiently and gestured to the drawing-room. 'I suggest we make ourselves comfortable before we start talking.'

In the drawing-room there was further evidence of his impatient vigil. A couple of cups and glasses, their contents half consumed. Newspapers and magazines impatiently tossed aside.

With a prickle of anxiety Shiona sat down. What the devil was going on?

Jake picked up his half-empty glass of whisky, knocked back the contents, and pulled off his tie, flinging it over the back of the sofa beside his discarded jacket.

'I'll go first,' he told her with a scathing smile. 'Since I've come all this way, I think I deserve that honour.'

Shiona could feel the tension in her growing, taut as the strings of a violin. He was acting so strangely. He seemed racked with emotion. She had never seen him like this before.

Then he floored her completely as, in a voice stiff with anger, he demanded, 'Why the hell didn't you tell me about Ryan?'

For a moment she simply stared at him. Then stupidly, she answered, 'Tell you what about Ryan?'

His eyes were like meat-hooks, tearing into her. 'The truth,' he said harshly. 'That would've done for a start.'

Shiona felt herself pale. Her skin was prickling uncomfortably. 'You mean you know the truth about Ryan?'

'Yes, finally I do.' His eyes drove into her. 'At least three years too late to be able to help him.' His tone was accusing, thick with emotion. 'What the hell made you think you had the right to keep the facts about my brother from me?'

Shiona swallowed, wishing she had a drink. She licked her lips. 'It wasn't my decision. Ryan made me promise never to tell you.'

'And you kept a promise—to a *junkie.*' He emphasised the word with hurt and loathing. 'You put a promise to a junkie before your duty to me?'

'What duty to you? I had no duty to you! Your brother may have been a junkie, but he was also my friend and I happened to love him! My duty was to honour the promise I made to him!'

'Your duty was to inform his family!' Overcome with anger, Jake sprang to his feet, looking as though he longed to demolish the room about him. 'If we'd known, my father and I might have been able to help him! Didn't you ever think of that?'

'Yes, I thought of that!' Shiona sprang to her feet, too, her emotions suddenly overwhelming her. 'But he didn't want you to know! He was desperately ashamed! The only one he wanted to help him was me!'

The pain in Jake's face was making her heart weep. She took a step towards him, her eyes beseeching. 'I was a stranger, remember, not really one of the family. It was easier for him to come to me.'

'A stranger. . .' He nodded. Then he turned away from her. She saw his shoulders lift and fall as he sought to gain control of himself. Then he said in a quiet voice, 'Some damned stranger. According to what I've been told, you were his saviour.'

He turned round slowly, his eyes burning into her. 'I've spoken to the doctors at the hospital where he was treated, and they've told me the whole long, miserable story. How you stood by him when he was at his very lowest, how you continued to believe in him when no one else did.'

He shook his head slowly, breathing in deeply. 'You were his "guiding light", his "will to survive". That was how one of the doctors described you. You were the one who never deserted him, in spite of the horrors he put you through. You took all of the abuse, the failures and disappointments, and kept on coming back for more. And you did all of this without a word to anyone. . .' His voice trailed to a halt. He closed his eyes.

Shiona was trembling uncontrollably. She longed to reach out a hand to comfort him, but her muscles refused to obey her brain.

'I only did what anyone else who loved him would have done. You would have done the same if you'd known.'

As he opened his eyes and smiled at her strangely, she added, 'And it was worth it in the end. He kicked the habit, as his doctors must have told you. He'd been off drugs for six months when he died in that fire.'

Jake nodded. 'I know.'

'And I'm sure he would have stayed off.'

'With you around to help him, I've no doubt he would.'

'Even without me. He'd grown much stronger. He was determined to make something decent out of his life.'

Jake was looking at her as though it was the first time he had really seen her. He took a step towards her and touched his hand to her cheek. Then he frowned, and there was a note of torment in his voice

as he demanded roughly, shaking his head, 'For
God's sake, Shiona, why didn't you tell me?'

'I couldn't. I told you, I promised Ryan.'

He took a deep breath. 'How can you forgive me?'

She felt his fingers tremble lightly against her
cheek.

'All those things I've said to you. All those awful
accusations. How could you go on letting me think
that they were true?'

'It wasn't easy.' Her flesh was melting beneath his
fingers. She looked into his eyes and felt herself
drowning.

'My poor, dear Shiona.' He was stroking her hair,
as though to stroke away all the hurt he had inflicted.
'All that money I thought he was spending on you,
he was spending on drugs. I ought to have guessed.'

'How could you have guessed? You had no reason
to believe it. Even I didn't believe what was going on
at first. I knew that some of his friends were into
drugs, but I didn't know Ryan was until he collapsed
on me one day. That was when he begged me to
move in with him to try and help him. He was
desperately trying to kick the habit on his own, but
he needed moral support and someone to keep an
eye on him. A sort of policeman-cum-nursemaid,
that's what I was really.'

'My dear Shiona, you were his saviour.' Jake
continued to stroke her hair. 'He would never have
made it if it hadn't been for you. And, as his brother,
that puts me in your debt, too.'

Shiona smiled with sheer joy. It was the most
wonderful thing to hear Jake finally say such things.

To know that he knew the truth at last. To feel him touching her, to see him looking at her with his heart washed clean of all the old hatred.

She looked into his face. 'But how did you find out? And on the very day I planned to tell you myself?'

'I found out by accident.' His eyes were hard again for an instant. 'If fate hadn't intervened, I might never have known.'

Then his expression softened once more. With both hands he framed her face. 'It was all thanks to a woman at the meeting today that I had my first inkling of what had really been going on.'

He had moved very close to her now, their bodies almost touching. Shiona swallowed hard. 'What woman? Who was she?'

'Her name's Marion Ritchie. She was a neighbour of yours and Ryan's in London. She's been back in Scotland for several years now, and she didn't know that Ryan was dead. But for some reason she knew he was my brother, and she asked me how he was keeping these days.'

His hands slipped to Shiona's shoulders. He made a face. 'There was something about the way she asked it that made me suspicious. When I probed a bit, rather reluctantly she told me that she understood he'd had an "illness", and was a regular outpatient at a local hospital.'

Shiona was frowning. 'I remember Marion Ritchie, but she was never a close friend. How could she have known anything about Ryan?'

'Alas, neighbours often know a great deal more

than we think they know. She knew he was an addict, I'm certain of that, though she didn't actually come out and say so to me. Still, I managed to get her to tell me the name of the hospital, and then I spent my entire lunchtime talking to the doctors there who treated Ryan.

'I'll tell you one thing.' He made a face. 'The afternoon meeting went right over my head. All I could think about was getting back to speak to you.' The fingers on her shoulders momentarily tightened. 'It was my intention, my dear Shiona, to tear you apart.'

He sighed and gathered her to him. She could feel his heart beating. 'Do you think you'll ever be able to forgive me?'

'I already have.' Her own heart was pounding. 'How could you judge? You didn't know the truth.'

'But I *did* judge,' he insisted. 'And I judged unfairly. I wouldn't blame you in the slightest if you never forgave me.'

'But I do forgive you. Absolutely.' She raised her eyes to him and smiled. 'Anyway, it was partly my fault. I could have told you if I'd wanted to. After all, you gave me endless opportunities.'

He sighed and let his hands slide round her shoulders, drawing her even closer towards him. 'I always sensed there was something you weren't telling me. That was why I kept pushing you and provoking you—to try and make you spit it out. But the more you refused to say anything, the more I began to believe that maybe there was nothing to tell, after all.'

'I longed to tell you.' Shiona shook her head. 'I could scarcely bear for you to believe what you did.'

'And yet, out of loyalty to Ryan, you let me.' Gentle fingers stroked her hair, sending helpless shivers across her scalp. 'I was also wrong about you and my father—though I had actually begun to suspect that years ago. I know how compulsively generous my father was. He was a man who wouldn't take no for an answer. But when all this business about you and Ryan cropped up, it sort of renewed all my earlier suspicions.'

He sighed a harsh sigh. 'What an idiot I've been!'

Shiona gazed with compassion into his face. 'We all make mistakes. I'm just glad it's straightened out.'

Jake drew back to look at her. 'You know, you're quite a girl.' Still watching her, he reached for one of her hands and pressed the warm palm against his lips. 'Quite a girl,' he repeated softly. 'And I was so blind I couldn't see it.'

Shiona felt her heart perform a triple somersault and lodge itself somewhere in the region of her throat. She swallowed and wondered if she should pull her hand away, but as Jake continued to hold it against his cheek, watching her with eyes that suddenly threatened to swallow her, she was aware that all at once her hand had become paralysed. In fact, every inch of her was quite incapable of movement.

With his free hand he was softly pushing back her hair, sending goosebumps scattering from Shiona's head to her toes. She shivered inwardly, a delicious sensation, and felt her heart break into a gallop.

Whatever was about to happen, she knew she could not stop it.

Jake stroked her hair. 'My flame-haired temptress.' There was a strange smile playing round his lips. 'My beautiful, unpredictable, flame-haired temptress. What a very special person you've turned out to be.'

Shiona found her voice. 'I'm not so special. I'm not special in the slightest, as a matter of fact.' Perhaps she could convince him to stop looking at her that way—though, in her heart, she did not want to stop him.

'Oh, yes, you are.' His fingers scorched her as they trailed through her hair, making her spine tingle. 'What you did for my brother was very special. I shall always be in your debt for that.'

His fingers stilled suddenly. He frowned for a moment. 'And the strength it took to keep your secret to yourself is the kind of strength that very few possess. Take my word for it. . .' he smiled unexpectedly, lighting her heart with an unspeakable pleasure '. . .you are a very special person indeed.'

I love you. The thought went exploding through Shiona's head, winding her, driving the strength from her body. I love you. I love you. The words kept repeating themselves until she was afraid he must be able to hear them.

Shiona closed her eyes and forced the thought from her. Where had such perfect madness come from?

When she opened her eyes again, Jake's were burning down at her. They seemed to pierce into her like rods of blue fire. She tried to move away, but still she was paralysed. And then she felt his arm slide round her waist.

'My dear Shiona. . . My sweet Shiona. . .'

The way he spoke her name twisted her stomach into knots. And the way his hand was pressed against her back was turning her limbs to pillars of sawdust.

As he drew her close to him, she let herself fall against him. And it was as though someone had peeled away the skin from her nerve-ends. Suddenly her senses were up in flames.

Just the touch of his chest pressing hard against her breasts, just the lightest fleeting brush of his thighs against hers, and suddenly her heart was weeping from the wanting of him. Her hands trembled as they fluttered to rest against his shoulders.

He murmured something, but she did not catch the words. The thundering in her heart had grown so enormous that she would not have heard a thing had there been an earthquake. But she saw his lips move and her eyes fixed on them, for suddenly she hadn't the courage to look into his eyes. There was something in their depths that seemed to devour her—and her own eyes, she feared, revealed the torment of her soul.

The hand in her hair was caressing her gently, and imperceptibly tilting her face towards his. She felt her head go back and her lips part with anticipation. Then, for one breathless moment, the whole world stood still.

'Shiona!'

She felt rather than heard him say her name. Then she died a thousand deaths and was born again instantly as at last his lips came down to cover hers.

It was just as she had dreamed in her dreams it would be—a blissful sensation that shot down to her toes and sent her blood, like fiery rapids, exploding through her veins. But she could never have imagined the bright colours that filled her brain—a vivid, intoxicating, shifting kaleidoscope of wonder and pleasure and excitement and joy.

I love you! I love you! Her arms circled his neck, as the words roared unstoppably inside her head. She caressed his hair and slid her hands along his shoulders, her heart threatening to burst from the ferocity of her emotions.

And his hunger, as he kissed her, seemed as powerful as her own. There was a passion in his lips and a fire in his caresses that filled her heart to overflowing. His desire for her was as real as her own. She could feel the power of it consume him.

As his lips moved against hers, burning, arousing, Jake's hands swept the warm, receptive curves of her body. And Shiona pressed herself against him, enthralled by the hard feel of him, her body responding to every little touch.

His hands brushed her breasts, already ripe beneath her blouse, sending shafts of electricity darting through her. With a sigh she slid her hands beneath the front of his jacket and let her own fingers graze the hard stubs of his nipples.

He groaned and drew her closer, one hand around her waist, while the other separated her blouse from

the waistband of her skirt. Then his hand was slipping beneath the soft silk fabric, making her flesh
jump excitedly as he touched her, and his fingers
were reaching for the strap of her bra, dropping it
loosely over her shoulder and peeling the cup of her
bra away.

An instant later her breath caught in her throat and
a hopeless shaft of longing went writhing through
her loins, as he cupped the weight of her breast in
his palm and strummed the burgeoning nipple, till it
ached, with his thumb.

Shiona gasped from the sheer extravagance of the
sensations shooting through her. It was almost too
much pleasure to bear. And yet, if he were to stop,
she would have to cry out in protest. The agony of
such a torment would tear her to shreds.

Without even realising what she was doing, she
had undone the buttons of his shirt and was sliding
her hand now against his naked chest. She let her
hands rove over the hard, smooth muscles with their
central sprinkling of rough dark hairs, and as she
breathed in she could smell the clean male scent of
him. She shivered and pressed her lips against his
skin. Warm and delicious. Utterly intoxicating.

He was kissing her hair, her brow, her ears, then
bending to kiss the hollow of her neck, and she could
feel the breathing in his throat growing harsher and
his hunger thrusting hard between his legs.

Love me! Please love me!

She longed to say it. To fall down on the sofa and
tear off her clothes and beg him to make wild,

abandoned love to her. She longed to feel his nakedness pressing against her, to feel his strength as he entered her, to feel his power as he consumed her. And her heart was crying out, Oh, Jake, I love you!

It was as though he had sensed her unspoken pleading. He pulled her close, his arms tight around her, and buried his face for a moment in her hair.

'You know where this is leading?' His voice was a harsh murmur. 'You know what's going to happen if we continue with this?'

'I don't care.' Her face was pressed against him, so that the words were swallowed against his chest. She strained to look up at him. 'I don't care,' she repeated. 'I want it to happen. More than anything.'

He groaned and did not look at her. 'I want it, too.' Then he smiled lop-sidedly. 'But then, I scarcely have to tell you. I'm sure you're perfectly well aware of that.'

'Then there's nothing to stop us.' Her voice was a whisper. Her heart was pounding in her chest.

But he was shaking his head again, making her soul freeze. 'I wish that were true, but we both know it isn't.'

He didn't have to say why. Shiona knew. It was Janice. He couldn't be unfaithful to the mother of his child.

Her heart turned over sickly. 'Of course,' she conceded. 'I was being crazy. You're absolutely right.'

As his grip on her loosened, she took a step back, and it was as though a cold wind suddenly whistled all around her. Adjusting her blouse and dropping her eyes away, she wrapped her arms protectively around herself. Her soul ached. Suddenly they were on different planets.

Shiona felt him sigh as he laid his hands on her shoulders. 'I think it would be wise if I went straight back to Edinburgh. It would simply be asking for trouble for me to spend the night here.'

Shiona nodded in response. 'Absolutely.' Then her heart seemed to crack as his hands slipped away.

She looked up into his face, fighting back the urge to reach out her hand and stop him from going. Then she heard herself murmur, 'There are things I have to say. . .about Janice. . .about Kirsty. . . That was partly why I wanted to see you.'

But he was turning away. 'Not now, Shiona.' And suddenly there was a darkness about his demeanour. All at once he seemed terribly far away.

She started to protest. Her heart was crumbling.

But he cut in almost roughly, 'Goodnight, Shiona.' Then, on sharp, swift strides he was heading for the door, while Shiona continued to stand where she was, rock still, as though rooted to the floor.

She continued to stand there, eyes closed tightly, long after the front door had closed behind him and she had heard his car disappear down the drive.

And suddenly wolves were howling in her head.

All she could think was, I love you! I love you!

Over the next few days it became clear that Jake was avoiding her. Whenever Shiona phoned—at the office or at his home—she was told that he was unavailable. And when she tried several times to pin him down at the office, invariably, as if he were telepathically aware of her intentions, he was elsewhere.

What was he up to? Shiona wondered through the desperate sadness that consumed her. Was this perhaps his way of trying to tell her that he deeply regretted what had passed between them? Was he afraid she might try to push for more?

He needn't have feared, she thought to herself sadly. A single kiss never changed the world, and she was all too aware of the reality of the situation. Jake was tied to Janice by their unborn baby. He could never be Shiona's, even if he wanted her, and there was nothing to indicate that he really did.

So he had no need to hide. She would not have pushed him. Wasn't she used by now to disguising her love for him? She smiled to herself bitterly. She'd had years of practice. Years of pretending that her love had turned to hate.

But it had all been a bluff. She realised that finally. A bluff she had perpetrated mainly on herself to give herself the strength to go on living. But she had never really hated him, though she had sincerely wanted to. The only emotion she had ever truly felt for him was love.

So what would happen next? she wondered bleakly. Would she have to face him across a court and wrangle with him in public over custody of Kirsty? The thought appalled her more now than ever. But what choice did she have if he was determined to oppose her? And it seemed that he was. He would not even speak to her.

In the meantime Kirsty had made a full recovery.
On her daily trips to Edinburgh to try to pin Jake
down, Shiona made a point of seeing her little sister,
and she was delighted at how well she was looking,
even though, as yet, she wasn't back at school.

'Will I still be able to spend Easter at Carol's?'
Kirsty enquired anxiously one day. Then she'd added
swiftly, 'Dr Fraser says I'm well enough.'

'I'll have to check with him—and with Uncle Jake.'
Shiona bent to kiss the anxious little brow. She had
almost forgotten about the long-standing arrange-
ment with Kirsty's best friend Carol's parents for
Kirsty to spend a couple of weeks with them at
Easter.

'I really want to go,' Kirsty assured her. 'I really
like it on the farm.'

It turned out that Dr Fraser was in favour of the
idea. 'A bit of country air will do her the world of
good.'

And, according to Mrs Aitken, Jake had no objections, so arrangements were made for Carol's parents
to pick up Kirsty on the appointed day.

And still Shiona had failed to pin down Jake,
despite the fact that, out of desperation, she had
taken up residence at his Edinburgh home. The latest
development, according to his secretary, was that he
was out of the country.

'He's gone to Holland on business for a few days.'

And then, out of the blue, as she was getting ready
for bed on the evening before Kirsty was due to go
off on holiday, Mrs Aitken tapped on Shiona's bedroom door.

'There's a call for you,' Miss Fergusson. It's Mr MacKay.' She handed her the phone. 'You'd best take it in your room.'

For an instant Shiona was overcome by a sense of total confusion. Just the thought of talking to him, the thought of hearing his voice had caused her heart to leap to her throat.

But she managed a composed smile as she took the phone. 'Thank you.' She nodded and closed the door.

Then she seated herself on the edge of the bed and, breathing deeply, raised the phone up to her ear. 'Hello? This is Shiona. I'm glad you've phoned. As you know, I've been trying to get hold of you all week.'

'I'm sorry about that.'

He sounded far away—spiritually, as well as in terms of actual distance.

'I'm phoning to tell you something that should please you. . .' He paused for an instant before continuing, 'I won't be contesting your claim for custody.'

Shiona could not believe her ears. For a moment she was speechless, then she said, 'You mean you're happy for Kirsty to come and live with me?'

He gave a bitter laugh. 'I'd rather she lived with me. But yes, I'm happy for her to live with you. Now that I know the truth about everything. . .' there was a note of apology in his voice as he said it '. . . I'm convinced you'll make her an excellent mother.'

'But what about——?'

She had intended to say, 'What about you and

Janice?', but before she could finish the sentence he had cut in to tell her,

'I'm in London, at Heathrow Airport on a stop-over. But I expect to be back in Scotland within the next couple of weeks, so we can discuss whatever needs to be discussed then. I understand from my solicitor that the custody hearing won't be till after the Easter holidays, so we have plenty of time.

'But I have to go now. They're calling my flight. Give Kirsty my love.'

Then he hung up.

Shiona frowned at the phone in total bewilderment. What on earth had all that been about? she wondered. And what on earth had brought on his sudden change of heart?

She laid down the phone and leaned back against the pillows. She suspected she knew the answer to that second question. The reason Jake had had a change of heart was because he had finally realised for himself that Janice would not make a good mother for Kirsty, and that Shiona, on the other hand, would. He loved the child enough, after all, to give her up.

Warm pride surged through her. She smiled to herself. He had done what was right without having to be pushed. But then, hadn't she always known that he was a good and decent man?

She pushed the thought from her. Such thoughts were too painful. She must not dwell on his good points. She must simply forget him.

And the best place to do that, it suddenly struck her, was London. Back at work, in her studio, surrounded by all her friends and workmates. There was nothing to keep her here, after all, for the moment. Kirsty was going off tomorrow to Carol's and, as Jake had said, the custody hearing would not be scheduled till after Easter.

Shiona felt suddenly strengthened by her decision. It would do her psyche good to get away from here, even just for a couple of weeks. By the time she came back, with any luck, she would have emerged from her current emotional upheaval, able at least to *act* with indifference towards Jake.

He had said he'd be back within a couple of weeks. Where was he off to? she wondered briefly. No doubt on some other business assignment. But it wasn't important. All that was important was that she leave here immediately, as soon as Kirsty had gone to Carol's, and start working on driving him out of her heart.

She got up from the bed and started packing, throwing things haphazardly into her bag.

But all the will-power she could muster could not shut out the desolate sense of emptiness that had closed like a cold hand round her heart.

CHAPTER NINE

'Here's to Paris!'

'And to the collection!' Desmond grinned across the restaurant table at Shiona as they clinked champagne glasses together. 'I just know it's going to knock these Parisians dead!'

Shiona laughed. 'It certainly ought to, considering all the work that we've put into it!'

'You mean all the skill and talent that *you've* put into it! *You're* the one who deserves the honours!'

Shiona smiled across at him. 'It's been a team effort. You know that.' But all the same she felt a flash of gratitude for the wonderful way Desmond had kept up her morale over the past ten emotionally tormented days. If it hadn't been for Desmond she would never have got through them.

On her first day back at the studio, he had taken one look at her, pulled a sympathetic frown, and told her sternly, 'What you need, my girl, is to get down to some hard work and chase from your head whatever it is that's bothering you.'

Then he had reached out and pulled her into his arms and held her tightly for a moment. 'Tell me about it, if you think it'll help you. You know I'm famous for being a good listener.'

Helplessly Shiona had wept against his shoulder, overcome by his simple kindness and concern. 'I'll

168

tell you about it later,' she had promised. 'But right
now, I think you're right. Work is what I need.'

In fact the Paris gala was weeks away and they
needn't have rushed into finalising the preparations.
But as Desmond had said, 'There's no harm in being
ready early. It gives us the chance to change things if
we decide to.'

And so, now, just ten days after her return from
Loch Lomond, all the garments and accessories were
miraculously ready, and Shiona and her number two
were enjoying one of their celebratory dinners.

'Hard work agrees with you. You're looking terrific,' Desmond announced as he sipped his champagne. 'If you ask me, you look fit for anything—
even a face to face with you-know-who!'

'Jake?' Shiona smiled and pulled a face. 'Yes, I'm
feeling a whole lot better. I think I've finally managed
to come to terms with that débâcle.' She took a
mouthful of her drink. 'And then there's Kirsty. . .
Thinking about her, making plans to be her
mother. . .' Her face glowed with pleasure. 'That's a
wonderful thing.'

She sighed an inward sigh. Her emotions were so
confused. On the one hand she was filled with total
elation at the prospect of soon having Kirsty with
her. But at the same time that emptiness in her heart
still haunted her, that emptiness that only Jake could
fill. Perhaps, she had finally decided, I shall simply
have to learn to live with it.

Desmond cut through her thoughts. 'If you ask
me, that Jake of yours must be totally blind, not to

say crazy. Fancy throwing up the chance of a girl like
you! What he needs is his head examined!'

'It's me who needs my head examined!' Shiona
frowned and stared down into her champagne glass.
'Fancy falling in love with the same man twice—
when I knew he could never be interested in me!'

'He sounded interested enough from what you
told me. Or at least not entirely indifferent, shall we
say?'

Shiona shook her head. 'That was just one of these
things.' She knew he was referring to her last meeting with Jake and that explosive love scene in the
drawing-room, only the sketchiest version of which
he'd been privy to. She herself had thought about it
often throughout many a long and sleepless night,
tormenting herself by reliving each sweet moment,
yet knowing it would be wiser just to forget it.

She raised her eyes to Desmond's. 'It didn't mean
anything. And besides,' she added, 'he's probably
married by now.'

It had struck her that perhaps that was where Jake
had been going that night he'd called her from
Heathrow Airport—on a secret brief honeymoon
with Janice after a quick, quiet register office wedding. In fact, the more she had thought about it the
more convinced she had become.

As she bit her lip, Desmond recognised her pain,
and reached out sympathetically to touch her hand.
'You'll forget him. You'll see,' he assured her, smiling
gently. 'One day you'll fall in love again.'

Shiona nodded. 'Of course I'll fall in love again.'
Though she didn't believe it for a moment. The only

man she had ever loved was Jake. She suspected she was incapable of loving any other.

Her friend squeezed her arm and winked across at her. Then his expression brightened as he gently changed the subject. 'Let's talk a little more about the Paris gala. . .'

It was late—after eleven—when they left the restaurant, and they decided to share a taxi.

'We'll drop you off first,' Desmond suggested.

But Shiona insisted, 'Don't be silly. It makes much more sense to drop you off first.'

'But I prefer to see you safely to your flat. A young lady like yourself needs looking after.'

'I can look after myself.' Shiona wouldn't hear of it. 'Don't worry, I'll be perfectly OK on my own.'

Famous last words, she thought to herself, as she stepped out of the lift on to the second-floor landing of the luxury block of flats where she lived. Though the landing was empty and there wasn't a sound all around, she had the strangest sensation that someone was there.

The entrance to her own flat was down one of the narrow corridors that led off from the rectangular landing, and as she stepped towards it she noticed with sudden uneasiness that one of the wall lights halfway down the corridor had gone, plunging the passageway into semi-darkness. All at once she was wishing that Desmond was with her.

Don't be silly! she chided herself with impatience. You come home alone every night of your life! What are you suddenly so afraid of?

But she had barely gone two steps along the

corridor when something moved out of the shadows. The tall, threatening figure of a man. Her heart flew to her mouth as she yelped and turned tail.

'Stop! Come back!' a man's voice was calling. She could hear footsteps striding along the corridor behind her.

But she kept on running, as panic overtook her, and didn't stop until she was back at the lift.

'Shiona! It's me!' As her finger jabbed the button, suddenly a firm hand was on her sleeve. 'I'm sorry I scared you. I didn't mean to.' He swung her round. 'Shiona, it's me!'

Her heart was almost jumping out of her ribcage. She stared at him breathlessly, unable to speak. Then she sighed and swallowed. 'Jake!' she breathed.

He held her by the shoulders, his grip firm and comforting. 'I've been waiting for you for the past three hours, pacing the corridors, wearing out the carpet. I didn't mean to give you a fright like that.'

Shiona smiled shakily, as her shock turned to bewilderment. What on earth was Jake doing here?

He had dropped his hands down from her shoulders and slipped them into his trouser-pockets. 'I know it's late, but I want to talk to you.'

'What about?' Shiona was still standing by the elevator, watching him with suspicious hazel eyes. There was something odd about him, an air of uncertainty, a dark, worried look at the back of his eyes. Then a thought suddenly occurred to her. She felt a dart of panic. 'Is it something to do with Kirsty? Has something happened to her?'

'It's nothing to do with Kirsty. Kirsty's fine.' He

smiled reassuringly and for a moment his expression
softened. Then once more the deep blue eyes grew
serious. 'Do you think we can go to your flat now
and talk?'

She wanted to say yes. She wanted to take hold of
him and throw herself recklessly into his arms. But
at the same time, for her sanity's sake, she knew she
must say no while she still had the strength to do so.

She averted her gaze. 'I'd rather not. It's much too
late and I'm extremely tired.'

'Please?'

Shiona blinked. Had she heard him say please?
She swallowed awkwardly. 'Can't it wait until
tomorrow?'

'It could, but I'd much rather talk to you now. I've
come all the way from Loch Lomond just to see you.
It won't take long. No more than half an hour.' He
smiled persuasively. 'Then I promise I'll leave.'

Her will was broken. There was no way in the
world she could deny that earnest, almost pleading
look in his eyes.

Shiona sighed, defeated. 'OK, then. But remember
you promised half an hour.'

Jake nodded. 'As soon as I've told you what I've
come for, I promise you can throw me out.'

They walked down the corridor in single file,
Shiona leading the way to her front door. Then, once
inside the sitting-room, she bade him take a seat.
'I'm going to have a drink. What will you have?' she
offered.

He nodded. 'I'll have a whisky with just a dash of
water.' Then he sat down on the sofa and looked

around him. 'This is a pretty nice place you've got here,' he told her.

'Thank you. I like it,' Shiona answered over her shoulder, as she poured a whisky for him and a brandy for herself. It wasn't like Jake to make small talk, she was thinking. What on earth was going on?

She crossed the carpet and handed him his whisky, then seated herself in the armchair opposite him, smoothing her slim skirt over her knees. And she found her eyes drifting to examine his left hand, noting that as usual he was wearing no rings, hating the way hope stirred foolishly for a moment.

Almost as though to punish herself for that foolishness, she forced herself to look him in the eye and enquire, 'So, how is Janice enjoying married life?'

He paused for only an instant. 'I can't really speak for her, but I would imagine she's enjoying it.'

His words were like a body-blow. Momentarily, Shiona felt winded. Suddenly she realised just how much she'd been hoping that Jake and Janice were still not married.

She swallowed the mountain that had lodged in her throat and asked with thin sarcasm, 'Why, hasn't she told you?'

'As a matter of fact, she hasn't. But then, she hasn't had an opportunity.' His eyes, as he spoke, were strangely shuttered. 'I haven't seen her since the wedding.'

'How very peculiar.' Shiona's breathing was ragged. She felt like jumping to her feet and asking him to leave instantly. This conversation was proving to be unbearably painful. Each word he uttered was a knife in her heart.

'What's the matter?' she enquired. 'Aren't you speaking?'

He shook his head. 'We haven't spoken since the wedding.'

Shiona frowned. He was starting to confuse her. Then he smiled lop-sidedly and confused her even further. 'She's currently in Mexico on her honeymoon.'

'Honeymoon?'

'Honeymoon.'

She was lost completely. 'So why aren't you with her?' Shiona peered across at him. 'Don't tell me she's honeymooning alone?'

'Absolutely not.' Jake sat forward in his seat. 'She's with her husband, just as she should be.'

Suddenly the room had become a total blur and Shiona's limbs felt as though they belonged to someone else. She laid down her glass before she dropped it. 'Would you kindly explain to me what you're talking about?'

'It's very easy.' Jake's eyes were on her. 'Janice has married someone else.'

'Someone else?' She could not believe it. 'But she told me she was pregnant with your baby!'

'Pregnant, yes, but not with *my* baby. I'm sure she never told you that. The father is the man who she's just married.'

Shiona sank back limply in her seat. 'You'll have to explain. I'm lost,' she told him.

'It sounds complicated, I know, but it's really

pretty simple.' Jake took a long swig from his glass. 'I agreed to marry Janice to get her out of a fix. This man she's married finally came to his senses, but he was refusing to marry her at one point. She was in a desperate state because of the baby. She's not the type to be an unmarried mother.'

'So you offered to marry her? That was pretty good of you.'

Suddenly the whole story was perfectly clear to her. Shiona's eyes narrowed as she elaborated tartly, 'But, of course, the arrangement was handy for you, too. It meant that you would gain custody of Kirsty!'

He was silent for a moment. Then he nodded his head. 'It sounds pretty cold-hearted when you put it like that, but I love that little girl. I wanted to be her father——'

'Even at the cost of marrying a woman you didn't love?'

'That was what I thought——'

'How could you? You're despicable! To go to such lengths to stop me gaining custody!'

At her words, for an instant his expression hardened. 'You're right; at that stage I would have done almost anything to stop Kirsty falling into your hands. And at that stage, when I entered into the agreement, I believed that a marriage to Janice could have worked.'

What he was saying hurt Shiona more than she could ever have believed possible. How could he have behaved so cynically? Did this man whom she loved have no heart at all? Had her love of all these years been thrown away on a man who was incapable of loving in return?

She reached for her brandy glass, her fingers tight around it. 'How could you even contemplate marrying a woman like that?'

'Because I was blind. Because I was desperate to save Kirsty—and because I didn't realise what type of woman Janice was. But I soon found out—even before you told me—and I was totally appalled at what I'd done. I knew I could never inflict her as a mother on Kirsty, but I was totally trapped by the promise I'd made. When I tried to get out of it, she threatened suicide. I was caught in a trap of my own foolish making.'

He sighed a harsh sigh and leaned back in his seat. 'I knew there was only one thing I could do—find the father of Janice's baby and persuade him to marry her in my place.' He shook his head and stabbed his fingers through his hair. 'It took me weeks, but I finally did it. I finally tracked him down to Antwerp.'

Shiona's eyes were wide, mesmerised by his story. 'So that was the business that took you to Holland?'

Jake nodded. 'That's right. But when I got there, he'd already moved on to the Middle East. That was when I phoned you. I thought I'd lost him forever. I thought I was going to have to end up marrying Janice, after all.'

'But you found him?'

'In the end, I found him. It wasn't easy, but I persuaded him to do the right thing. Let's just say there was a small exchange of money.'

Shiona shook her head. She could scarcely believe it all. 'And how about Janice? How did she react?'

'She was over the moon. She's really in love with this guy. As you yourself so candidly pointed out, she was only marrying me for my money—and, of course, to get out of a fix.'

Suddenly it was all clear—except for one thing. Shiona frowned. 'But why, once you'd found out the truth about Ryan and me, didn't you drop your custody claim immediately? Why did you wait until you were in Holland?'

'Because up until then I was absolutely positive that I would eventually manage to get out of the marriage, and it was my plan to seek custody as a single person. It was only when I was in Holland that I had my first serious doubts that I might actually fail and have to marry Janice—in which case there was no way I would wish to claim custody.'

'I see.' But there was still something else that bothered her. 'But what if you hadn't found out about me and Ryan? What if you'd gone on believing the worst of me and into the bargain you'd ended up having to marry Janice? What would you have done about Kirsty then?'

'Don't make me think of that.' A pained look crossed Jake's face. 'I would have had to have come to some arrangement with Janice—separate houses, separate lives—and taken on the job of looking after Kirsty myself, even if it had meant giving up my job.' His eyes were fierce. Shiona could see he was serious. 'Don't worry, there was no way in the world that I would ever have allowed Janice to get anywhere near her.'

That made Shiona feel better. But then a new thought occurred to her. She took a nervous mouthful from her glass. 'Have you come here to tell me that you're going to fight me after all, now that Janice is no longer around?'

He shook his head. 'No, that's not why I've come here. We've already done more than enough fighting, you and I.' There was a momentary pause. His eyes were on her. Then he rose to his feet suddenly, taking her by surprise. 'I suppose you know all of this is your fault?' he accused her.

Shiona blinked up at him, a sudden nervousness within her. 'I don't know what you're talking about,' she defended.

'What I'm talking about is that secret of yours and Ryan's.' Suddenly he had crossed the gap between them. 'If you'd told me the truth about that years ago, none of this wretched business would have happened.' Then, before she could answer, he had reached down to take hold of her and was drawing her firmly to her feet.

He looked down into her face. 'If only I'd known the truth about you, Shiona, there would have been no need for me to keep running away from my feelings for you. I could have told you years ago how I feel about you instead of trying to pretend to myself that I felt nothing.'

Suddenly Shiona could not look at him. She fixed her eyes on his tie, though she could barely focus. 'I've always known how you felt about me,' she mumbled. 'I've never had the smallest doubt that you hated me.'

He laughed a harsh laugh and shook her impatiently. 'Liar! You know I've never hated you—though for years I've been wishing that I could!'

Her eyes swivelled up then. Was he making fun of her? But as his gaze meshed with hers she knew that he wasn't. There was pain in his face, anguish shining from his eyes. Her heart stilled as suddenly his grip on her tightened.

'For pity's sake, Shiona, don't you know I've always loved you?'

Love?

For a moment the universe tilted. She had to hold on tight to him or else she might fall off. And suddenly that cold void deep within her was running over with warmth and happiness.

She leaned against him.

'Oh, Jake! Oh, Jake!'

Much later they lay in one another's arms, at peace amidst a frenzied tangle of bedclothes.

Shiona snuggled happily against Jake's broad, hard chest, listening to the steady sound of his heartbeat. 'I love you,' she whispered. It felt wonderful to say it.

'And I love you.'

He had said it a hundred times over the past blissful hour together, and each time the sound of it had been even sweeter. Then he sighed and ran his fingers through her hair.

'What fools we've been to waste so much precious

time. All those years when we could have been together.'

Shiona glanced up at him, at the head of thick hair, so dark and glossy against the creamy pillow, at the sculpted curved nose, the wide, mobile mouth and those eyes of deepest darkest sapphire. 'It's pointless to regret things,' she told him, smiling. 'And, besides, I wouldn't have missed this moment for the world.'

He tousled her hair that tumbled over her shoulders in a wild, bright mane of warmest auburn. 'My beautiful temptress.' He leaned and kissed her, letting his hand slide over her breast. Then, as she shuddered, he held her for a moment against him. 'There will be many more moments like this,' he promised her.

Shiona closed her eyes and drank in the scent of him, the virile, masculine scent of love. And her stomach twisted as she relived deliciously the moments of passion they had so recently shared.

She felt a shudder deep inside her. How well, how wonderfully he had loved her.

They had arrived in the bedroom without knowing how they had got there. As though their need for one another, so long denied, had demanded finally to be fulfilled. Then they had been sinking on to the bed and, between kisses and caresses, peeling the clothes hungrily from one another, until at last they lay naked, side by side.

Then with love they had explored one another's bodies with hands that were urgent, yet full of tenderness, each touch a declaration of the joy that possessed them, each kiss an unspoken protestation of love.

Shiona had never known such perfect happiness. To be kissed in such a way and caressed in such a way, with so much love, by a man she adored. And inside her an unbearable excitement was building as they had moved towards that luminous moment when the two of them would finally be one.

When at last he'd come to her, his manhood hard against her, she held her breath and looked into his eyes.

'I love you,' he'd whispered and her heart stood still within her. Then she had gasped as he entered her and her poor heart burst with joy.

Surely it cannot be possible, she was thinking, to love anyone as intensely as I love this man.

Jake was kissing her now and stroking her hair. 'There will be many more such moments,' he repeated, smiling down at her. Then he frowned at her suddenly. 'How on earth could I be so crazy?'

'Crazy, you?' Shiona was smiling at him. 'Crazy isn't something I've ever thought you were.'

'Yet I am, nevertheless.' He gathered her to him. 'All these years I denied my love. All these years I tried to kill it.' He frowned into her face. 'I was so desperately afraid that you would turn out to be the sort of person who cares only about money and possessions.' He shook his head wryly. 'Like Janice, in other words.'

As Shiona touched his cheek, he paused for a moment. 'Did Ryan ever tell you about our mother?'

'Only that she died and that he loved her. He never told me any details.'

'Then let me tell you. It might help to explain things.' He rested his dark head against the pillows and gazed up at the ceiling as he spoke. 'Unlike my father, who had to work for his money, my mother was born into a very wealthy family. She always had everything she wanted. She never had to work a day in her life.'

He sighed. 'Let me tell you, that's not good for anyone. By the time she was thirty she was a bored, disgruntled woman whose only interest in life was squandering money. But that didn't make her happy. She started drinking heavily. Eventually she became an alcoholic.' He flicked a pained look in Shiona's direction. 'You were probably told that she died of a heart attack—but she didn't. What she died of was acute liver failure.'

There was a momentary silence. Shiona stroked his furrowed brow. 'Just like Ryan with his drugs,' she said quietly. 'He went the same way as your mother.'

Jake drew in breath. 'I should have suspected, but I thought we'd both learned from the tragedy of our mother.' He exhaled impatiently. 'Poor Ryan. I wish I'd known. How I wish I could have helped him.'

Shiona touched his cheek. 'He wouldn't have let you. He would have hated it if you'd known he was an addict. He admired you so much.' She smiled gently. 'More than anything he wanted to be like you.'

'Like me?' Jake smiled wryly, disbelieving. 'Why on earth would he want to be like me?'

'Because you're so successful, so together. And because everything you've achieved, you've achieved on your own.'

Jake shook his head and smiled at her wryly. 'Yes, that was a bit of an obsession, I'm afraid. Right from the start I was utterly determined I wasn't going to fall into the trap of the idle, pampered, rich man's son. I would never have been able to respect myself if all I'd ever done was take from my father.'

Shiona sat up on her elbow and looked down into his face. 'Is that why you were so disapproving of my apparent readiness to exploit your father's generosity towards me?'

'I'm afraid it was.' He pulled a face. 'And I reckon it was all tied up with what happened to my mother.' He reached out to touch her hair, running his fingers through it. 'I should have recognised that you were a stronger character than that, and accepted your delight in the presents my father gave you for what it was—sheer, innocent pleasure.'

He leaned to kiss her face, his eyes dark and serious. 'Perhaps I also used these silly criticisms of mine as a kind of buffer against the way I was starting to feel about you. For even then I was falling in love with you, though you were little more than a child at the time.'

Shiona punched his arm playfully. 'I was sixteen! I hardly think you can call that a child!'

'Well, to me it seemed a child. I was twenty-four. I felt that falling in love with you at that stage would very definitely not be a good idea.' He turned away. 'And then, years later, when Ryan died with not a penny to his name, I jumped to all the wrong conclusions—and, of course, you let me. You never defended yourself.'

His voice caught in his throat as he turned to take hold of her and press her fiercely against his chest. 'You wonderful little fool. How much I love you. And how painful it's been at times to love you. I tried to stop, but I couldn't do it. You are etched in my heart. I couldn't erase you.'

Shiona hugged him and kissed him. 'I'm glad you couldn't. And I'm glad I couldn't. I'm glad I love you.'

'Thank heavens for Kirsty!' He smiled at her suddenly. 'If we hadn't got involved in fighting over Kirsty, we might never have found out how each of us really feels.'

Shiona made a face. 'I don't believe you. Surely you always knew that I was in love with you?'

'I swear I didn't. How could I have known it? After all, you never told me.'

'But it must have been obvious!' Shiona scowled at him. 'I used to behave like your adoring little slave girl!'

'Did you? I didn't notice.' He smiled at her roguishly. 'And do you plan on continuing to be my adoring little slave girl?'

'I'll think about it.' Shiona bit his ear. 'If you promise to be my slave in return.'

He laughed and kissed her. 'I can think of nothing

nicer. I shall be your slave, if you wish. And, of course, your husband.'

Shiona blinked at that.

'You have no choice but to marry me.' He smiled at her, teasing her. 'You owe it to Kirsty. She needs a mother *and* a father.' Then his expression sobered. 'Besides which, my dear Shiona, I've waited long enough for you, and I've just come all the way from Loch Lomond to propose to you. There's no way I intend to let you out of this bed until you've promised that you'll marry me.'

'Is that really what you came for?'

'That's really what I came for.' He kissed her face. 'And as I said, there's no way I'm going to let you out of this bed until I have your answer in the affirmative.'

'But I like this bed.' Deliberately, she teased him, though her heart was thundering with happiness inside her. 'I'm in no hurry to get out.'

'OK. Then let me put it another way.' Jake leaned across suddenly, pinning her arms against the mattress. 'I refuse to make love to you again until you've agreed to be my wife.'

'You heartless creature!' Shiona's eyes were shining. 'In that case, what choice do I have but to agree?' Then she stretched up to kiss him warmly on the lips. 'Besides, I love you. I want to be your wife.'

Jake gathered her to him and rolled over on his back, so that she was lying on her stomach on top of him. 'I've already made arrangements to cut down on my travelling, but what are we going to do about